TODA
ARM
AIR CORPS

PAUL BEAVER

TODAY'S
ARMY
AIR CORPS

PAUL BEAVER

Patrick Stephens
Wellingborough, Northamptonshire

©Paul Beaver 1987

First published in 1987

British Library Cataloguing in Publication Data

Beaver, Paul
Today's Army Air Corps.
1. Great Britain. *Army. Air Corps* — History
I. Title
358.4'00941   UG635.G7

ISBN 0-85059-892-3

Cover illustrations: Front *Lynx/TOW helicopter showing the
roof-mounted sight for the anti-tank missile system (Robin
Adshead).* **Back** *Scout helicopters of 666 Squadron, manned
by the Territorial Army, at Netheravon.*

*Patrick Stephens is part of the
Thorsons Publishing Group*

Printed in Great Britain by R. J. Acford, Chichester, Sussex

1 3 5 7 9 10 8 6 4 2

CONTENTS

INTRODUCTION AND ACKNOWLEDGEMENTS

In truth, the Army Air Corps — known to the rest of the British Army as 'Teeny Weeny Airways', TWA for short — is the least-known of the three British forces' aviation units. The Army Air Corps is 'teeny weeny' only in terms of the size of its past aircraft, however, not in terms of its ability and effectiveness. In recent years, it has grown in importance, playing a vital role in the post-Colonial campaigns of the 1960s and 1970s, with its true worth coming to light during the South Atlantic campaign in 1982.

That is not the whole story, however, because the Army Air Corps, which celebrated its thirtieth anniversary in September 1987, has a daily role safeguarding the peace in Cyprus and Belize, supporting the civil power in Northern Ireland and as a major 'teeth arm' of the North Atlantic Treaty Organisation on its Central front.

During the next decade or so, we shall see the Army Air Corps continue to grow in importance and ability with the introduction of the Light Attack Helicopter and an increasing role in support of Britain's Army anywhere in the world. In addition, future areas of important consideration will be the threat posed by potential enemy helicopters with an anti-helicopter role and the command/control of all battlefield helicopters, standardized through NATO for cross-boundary operations in support of each nation's forces NATO-wide.

Little has been written about the Corps so I hope that this account goes some way to redress the balance; it is not, though, a complete history of British Army aviation but rather a primer on today's force.

During the preparation of this book, I have received considerable assistance from the Director Army Air Corps, Major General David Goodman and his staff at the Headquarters Director Army Air Corps at Middle Wallop, Hampshire. General Goodman retired in April and handed over to Major General Leslie Busk, who will guide the AAC until the beginning of the next decade.

On the operational side, my thanks to go Brigadier David Canterbury, formerly Commander Aviation, British Army of the Rhine, and Brigadier Kit Jebens, formerly Commander Aviation, United Kingdom Land Forces. At the Directorate, Lieutenant Colonels Nick Hall and Wilf Hyde-Smith kindly sifted any errors of fact from my prose, but any faults in the book remain my responsibility and certainly the interpretation is mine.

At unit level, I was assisted in the preparation of the BAOR section by the kindness of Lieutenant Colonels Denzil Sharp, Jim Orde and David Cranston, Majors Peter Gick, Mike Stubbington and Andy Lees and the officers and men of 1, 3 and 4 Regiments Army Air Corps. Finally from the Army Air Corps side, I would like to thank my friends in 666 Squadron (Volunteers) and the various Command PROs and PIOs for their kind assistance.

Outside the Corps, Colonel Mike Hickey (Rtd) of *Defence Begins at Home* has been most helpful with notes and access to his in-Corps booklet, *The Army Air Corps, Past and Present*. In due course, we can expect to see a full history of the Corps from his pen.

As usual I have been able to count on the assistance of Ian Woodward (Westland), Philip Birtles (British Aerospace), R H Bojdys (DPR JSPRS Hong Kong), Lieutenant Colonel Peter Bishop (UKLF), Ian Commin (artist and illustrator), and Robin Adshead, Patrick Allen and David Oliver (photographers).

Paul Beaver
March 1987

A SHORT HISTORY OF ARMY FLYING

In 1957 the United Kingdom's Minister of Defence, Duncan Sandys, directed the (then) War Office (now part of the Ministry of Defence) to assume responsibility for the manning and operation of its own light aircraft for the purposes of reconnaissance, direction of artillery fire, and general liaison flying. As a result, the Army Air Corps came into being in its present form on 1 September of that year. The Army Air Corps was, in effect, an amalgamation of two types of light aircraft unit which had been active for some time under Royal Air Force control; Air OP squadrons, in which the pilots were officers of the Royal Artillery; and Light Liaison Flights, supplementary to the Air OP organization, whose pilots, drawn from all arms of the Army, were seconded to the Glider Pilot Regiment for their tours of flying duty. The Light Liaison Flights were formed after gliders had ceased to have an operational role and were introduced as a means of employing some high grade officers and NCOs (former glider pilots) who could readily be converted to powered light aircraft to undertake some of the roles into which Air OP had diversified. Each has a short but eventful history.

The Air Observation Post

The Journal of the Royal United Services Institute published an article in 1933 which had far-reaching consequences for the British military.

*For many years British Army aviation was based on the high-wing monoplane observation aircraft, like this Auster Mk 6. (*Museum of Army Flying*)*

It was written by Captain H. J. Parham of the Royal Artillery, and criticized the contemporary method of directing artillery fire from Army Co-operation aircraft and put forward a number of suggestions which were thought revolutionary.

In the inter-war years, the Royal Air Force was numerically weak, having been drastically cut back from an aircraft strength of over 20,000 in 1918 to 25½ squadrons, of which only two were available for Army Co-operation duties. Amongst the roles of these squadrons was artillery direction, which was conducted in Morse code over a one-way wireless using a simple artillery code; the gun battery acknowledged corrections sent by the pilot laying out coloured panels on the ground. That drill had been evolved in the First World War and remained unchanged during the next two decades.

Army Co-operation pilots were partly made up of army officers seconded to the air force and partly of air force career officers undertaking a duty tour. The basic operating procedure was a briefing for a gunnery shoot well behind the lines, which meant that there would be a considerable pause between the brief and the aircraft arriving on station. During the First World War, the delay did not matter but with the development of rapid types of warfare — the 'blitzkrieg' was only a few years away — it was outdated by the 1930s.

Captain Parham's solution was a light, unarmed aircraft, equipped with two-way radio at a forward position alongside the artillery battery command posts, flown by competent gunner officers using standard

*Early example of army co-operation by the Royal Flying Corps, army aviation in the First World War. A technician checks an aerial camera used to provide photographs of the German trench systems. (*Museum of Army Flying*)*

Although deemed unfit for air observation post duties during the Second World War, the Westland Lysander proved ideal for covert operations in Occupied Europe.

artillery fire direction procedures.

Another development came in 1934, when a number of aviation enthusiasts formed the Royal Artillery Flying Club at Larkhill on Salisbury Plain. The club secretary was Captain Charles Bazeley, who presided over a series of unofficial trials, using the club's light aricraft to develop Parham's thesis. So encouraging were the trials that in 1939 Captain Bazeley, himself a qualified Army Co-operation pilot, managed to persuade the War Office and the Air Ministry that official trials should be held, even with the RAF proviso that regular Army Co-operation aircraft were used.

These incuded the new Westland Lysander, a high-wing mono-plane designed specifically for its role. It had outstanding short take-off and landing and slow flying characteristics, but was far larger than anything Parham or Bazeley visualized. The trials were successful, but the pilots warned that the Lysander was unlikely to survive in modern war against determined fighter attack. This proved to be the case in the Battle of France in 1940 and the Lysander was moved too intelligence and special duties. However, the trials were successful enough to encourage the Air Ministry to purchase a handful of light aircraft for an experimental Air Observation Post (Air OP) Flight to be known as D Flight RAF. It was sent to France in April 1940 with the

Beach rendezvous: Auster and Jeep reconnaissance party, believed to be in the Far East.

intention of carrying out field trials but the German offensive prevented them being used.

Captain Bazeley's Flight was nearly wound up then and on a number of subsequent occasions, but he proved that low flying techniques and skilled pilots would make the lightweight, unarmed aircraft like the Taylorcraft surviable in the modern battlefield. However, the success of the D Flight trials resulted in the acceptance of the Air Op concept by the War Office and during 1941–45 some twelve Flights were formed, operating in every theatre of the land war.

The Royal Artillery provided the pilots and non-technical ground crews, while the RAF supplied the technicians, squadron adjutants, equipment officers and the aircraft for Air OP operations. These were successfully carried out in most theatres of the Second World War, including Italy, and after D-Day. The first unit operated in Tunisia in 1942, and a total of twelve were formed by the end of hostilities. The original Taylorcraft were replaced by the first of a long line of Austers.

The essential success of Air OP was that it gave the artillery observer mobility and a commanding view of the terrain which enabled him to direct and concentrate massive artillery fire power. This was often a battle-winning factor. In the Far East, a pilot of 656 (Air OP) Squadron took the surrender of the Japanese forces at Kuala Lumpur (now Malaysia), as he was the first Allied officer to appear on

Immediate post-War operations included Eritrea for 1910 Flight with these Auster AOP 6 overflying the Royal Air Force standard at Asmara, 1951, symbolizing the RAF's role in the development of army aviation. (Major John Dicksee)

the scene — which just goes to prove how far forward the Air OP Austers operated during the Second World War.

By the end of the war, over a hundred decorations for bravery had been awarded and the men of the twelve squadrons formed had been praised by Field Marshall Viscount Montgomery who summed up a briefing after VE-Day with his thoughts on Air Op: 'primarily an Air Op officer must be a good gunner — it is not difficult to teach him to fly.'

After the cut-backs of the immediate peacetime era, Air Op squadrons, now flying the Auster 4, 5 and 6, played a part in the various conflicts which have spoiled the peace since 1945. Austers were active in Indonesia (Dutch East Indies), Korea, Malaya, Borneo, Kenya and Aden.

The Air OP aircraft was destined to be replaced by the helicopter, which in turn might well be partially superceded by the remotely piloted helicopter for particularly dangerous spotting operations.

Fixed-wing army aircraft were replaced by helicopters around the world; this is an Auster graveyard in Borneo in 1967. (Robin Adshead)

Many will have to be convinced that the man in the cockpit giving fire directions can ever be replaced by a man watching a TV monitor behind the lines.

Gliders

The second half of the army aviation story prior to the formation of the Army Air Corps is the Glider Pilot Regiment. The Germans had used glider and other airborne troops in the attack on Belgium and the Netherlands in 1940. This impressed the new British Prime Minister, Winston Churchill, who immediately ordered the formation of a British airborne division.

The glider was cheaper to mass produce than troop-carrying aircraft, especially at a time of a shortage of air crew and when every large aircraft was needed for bomber and coastal command operations. The glider pilot was a true professional, not only required to have a detailed knowledge of aviation but also to be capable of fighting on the ground alongside his 'human cargo' after arrival at the landing site.

In September 1940, the month during which the Battle of Britain came to its climax, pilots from the British Army and the Royal Air Force began training in commandeered civilian gliders. By November the first military glider, the Hotspur, had been flown, followed by the Horsa and later the tank-carrying Hamilcar.

By late 1941, British Army officers and NCOs were trained as glider pilots and on 24 February 1942 the Army Air Corps was formed for the first time. Later the Corps took over the administration of the Parachute Regiment and the Special Air Service.

The first British glider operations were flown in the Sicily landings,

*Gliders played a major role in Second World War army aviation; these are Hotspur training gliders 'somewhere over England'. (*Museum of Army Flying*)*

where Lieutenant Colonel George Chatterton pushed the idea of glider operations. Chatterton has been accurately equated with Bazeley as a pioneer of army aviation and his enthusiasm is well illustrated by the fact that he was one of the first to volunteer for glider duties.

Prior to this first operational use of British gliders, the pilots were required not only to fly a totally new type of glider to the one on which they had been trained but also to assemble the US-designed Hadrian type prior to any air activity. This first operation was an important milestone in the development of the glider but it ranks as only a qualified success.

Amongst the more serious problems was the fact that the British glider pilots were let down by the inexperience of the US Army Air Force 'tug' pilots. Some 69 gliders, their pilots and soldiers, were released off the coast and landed in the sea and only twelve of 56 gliders which were released at the correct point managed to land within the target area.

One of the opening moves on D-Day, the liberation of Occupied Europe, was an important airborne assault by parachute and glider. It was enormously successful when two *coup-de-main* operations were staged against vital bridges across the River Orne and the Caen Canal. Men of the Oxfordshire and Buckinghamshire Light Infantry were landed after the small group of six gliders had made what would now be called a stealth approach across the French coast, with the

*One of the classic glider operations was the Caen bridge 'coup-de-main' on the morning of D-Day. (*Museum of Army Flying)

pilots navigating by dead reckoning and memorized details from aerial photographs.

Gliders later brought in artillery and supplies for the Airborne Brigade, helping to consolidate the positions captured during the night and in the early morning of 6 June 1944. The skill of the Glider Pilot Regiment can be summed up by the fact that 212 of 250 gliders used in the operation landed at the assigned landing zones after a hazardous cross-Channel flight. Many of the glider pilots who landed in Normandy were returned to their units for the next phases of the invasion of Europe.

In August 1944 the invasion of Italy was followed by the liberation of France, when gliders were used for limited attacks in the south of the country. Britanny was also a venue for a small operation before the most famous glider operation in British history.

It was at Arnhem that the glider hit the public's imagination. The military planning of the operation was based on the attempt to capture river bridges in the Netherlands, near the border with Germany, and allow a link-up of Allied armies before a final drive into the Third Reich; the British objectives included the bridge over the Rhone — called by some a 'bridge too far'. Some 698 British gliders were used in the assault to capture the bridge, Operation Market Garden, and amazingly 621 landed successfully but the physical limitations of the site prevented a massed assault. Although the actual landings were obviously successful, the casualties in the resultant land battle were terrible and the plan failed to give a victory. It was without doubt a heroic action.

It did not stop the operational use of gliders, but the lessons of the operation were duly learned for the Rhine crossings in Germany. Air and artillery support was arranged to coincide with an almost simultaneous series of landings codenamed Operation Varsity.

It was the final glider operation and the massed assault resulted in ninety per cent of the 440 gliders used successfully landing beyond the bridgehead which had been captured in an initial assault. Brigadier Chatterton, the Commander Glider Pilots, had devised a series of important tactical changes to the operational plan, including the use of company groups with their own controlled landing zones. The casualties were again high enough to cause concern, especially as the development of anti-aircraft artillery had reached a new peak with the introduction of quad systems able to put up a 'wall of lead'. Gliders were obviously also vulnerable to counter action in the air. Large transport aircraft, better supply systems and, by 1950, the helicopter, had made the role of the glider outmoded.

POST-COLONIAL OPERATIONS

Army flying learned much from the Second World War, especially in terms of how aircraft could be expected to perform in a major conflict, but also, because Air OP especially operated in almost all theatres, how aircraft could be utilized in limited campaigns. During the 1950s and 1960s, Britain, leaving behind its Empire and colonies was engaged in a number of 'brush fire' operations in which the fixed-wing aircraft and then the helicopter were most valuable.

Malaya

The Communist attempt to take-over Malaya (and later the independent state of Malaysia) resulted in a long and drawn-out but eventually successful campaign. Army aircraft, mainly in the shape of the ubiquitous Auster, had been employed in the Far East after Victory Against Japan Day in 1945, first to support the Dutch attempt to re-establish control of the Dutch East Indies, now Indonesia, and then, initially based in Singapore, to support peace-keeping operations in the Malayan Peninsula.

At the beginning of the 'Emergency' as it was known in 1948, the air support for the British Army was provided by a handful of Royal Air Force transport and strike aircraft, mainly left-over from the developments of the Second World War. Included in this force structure was 656 Air Observation Post Squadron, officially on the books of the RAF but manned by a variety of British Army officers (predominantly Royal Artillery pilots) and men, as well as RAF technicians. The unit was highly efficient and worked well, flying more than 22,000 hours with 34

*An Auster AOP 6 at Bosciosa, Eritrea during a detachment to one of the British police posts during post-colonial operations after the Second World War. (*Major Dicksee)

Austers in 1955 alone, and by 1960, as the security situation came under control, the total air time of the unit was over 250,000 hours.

The main role of these Auster aircraft was in support of anti-bandit reconnaissance across the length and breadth of the Malayan Peninsula, often fighting the tropical weather rather than the Communist insurgents below. The whole terrain was almost exclusive jungle with few airstrips and even fewer airfields. Contemporary reports suggest that pilots flew for 80 to 90 hours a month (more than twice the present NATO forces' average), often alone, looking for the terrorist camps and what were picturesquely called 'gardens', meaning the cultivations used to feed them as they were driven from the major settlements by the security forces.

Camps were attacked by infantry plodding in through the jungle, often led by Commonwealth Special Air Service teams and other units specially trained for jungle warfare. The Army Austers helped the attack teams navigate through the featureless jungle and called in the initial air strikes which often preceded a ground attack. Of course in certain situations where time was important, the Auster pilot would act as a forward air controller for air attacks mounted by the RAF, Fleet Air Arm and Commonwealth forces.

Both jet and piston-engined ground attack aircraft were used in the conflict, including Spitfires and Tempests of Second World War vintage and the later generation of Meteor and Venom. At one stage, the Royal Australian Air Force provided Avro Lincoln bombers developed from the wartime Lancaster and proceeded to bomb areas of jungle without effective control.

656 Squadron's Austers soon changed the situation and began guiding in the bombers using flares and radio direction; this happened around the clock and certainly caused considerable upset to the enemy on the ground. Auster target-marking techniques were also employed to assist the Dakota, Valetta and Bristol Freighters of the RAF and Royal New Zealand Air Force in dropping supplies, including mail, to garrisons and outposts. Leaflets were also dropped and this form of psychological warfare was rated as highly effective.

The number of operations mounted by 656 Squadron led to a policy of converting former Glider Pilot Regiment personnel, and non-Royal Artillery aircrew were employed in the Light Liaison Flights described elsewhere.

Korean interlude

Between 1951 and 1956 (after the Army Air Corps had been disbanded), as if the operatons in Malaya were not enough, Army aviators were employed with the Commonwealth Division fighting yet more Communist aggression in Korea. Two flights were attached to the Division, 1903 Air Observation Post and 1913 Light Liaison.

Artillery direction was undertaken and the traditional leaflet 'raids' were flown against North Korean and Chinese positions. The Austers were active throughout the conflict, which ended in 1953, and afterwards in the uneasy period of truce. They do not appear to have come up against enemy air attack but were certainly engaged by anti-aircraft fire, two aircraft being lost in action, and one crew was taken prisoner for the duration.

Cyprus

Another area of low-intensity conflict in the 1950s was Cyprus, the beautiful Mediterranean Island which is still plagued with sectarian strife. In 1957, the uneasy truce between warring Greeks and Turks, as well as between terrorist and British forces, broke down.

To provide air cover for the security forces, the two resident Army Air Corps flights were formed into a new squadron in May 1958, designated 653 Light Aircraft Squadron AAC and flying a mixture of Auster AOP 6 and 7 aircraft, based at such exotic locations as Nicosia and Kermia.

The major roles during the Cyprus troubles were reconnaissance, curfew-patrol and a certain amount of liaison flying for British Army and government officials. Operating at between 2,000 and 4,000 ft (610 and 1,220 m), the pilot and observer, equipped with standard binoculars, would identify trouble — riots, ambushes in preparation, etc — and guide in ground forces. In rural areas, the British Army used armoured car patrols and road blocks, whilst in the towns there were various units available to maintain the peace.

The Austers were very successful at spotting officially-established road blocks and are said to have contributed to a large number of arrests of wanted terrorists, arms smugglers and leaflet carriers. If a vehicle was spotted off the road or turning around having seen a vehicle check point, the ground forces could be called in to give chase and apprehend the suspects.

On the other hand, Austers flew in advance of the British forces' re-supply convoys taking food, fuel and other supplies to remote establishments in such areas as the Cyprus panhandle, north-east of Famagusta. The use of air power was extremely successful and almost all convoys with Auster top cover went about their business unmolested.

*Aircraft of 651 Squadron wearing United Nations markings in the period of tension after Independence in 1964. The Scout AH 1 helicopter (from 21 Flight) took over many of the roles of the Auster and is seen here patrolling the Kyrenia Pass. Beaver aircraft of 19 Flight were used for supply dropping and this particular aircraft is seen flying over the Nicosia Plain. This work was necessary to support UN observation posts and beleaguered small-holdings of either Greek Cypriots in Turkish areas, or vice versa. The Auster AOP 9 (21 Flight) was used in support of 16 Parachute Brigade during April and May 1964. (*Major John Dicksee*)*

In 1959, the London Agreement was signed which effectively brought peace to Cyprus and set up the government machinery for independence, 653 Squadron could then return to normal peacetime training operations, including the development of artillery spotting talents and genral army routines. With the stablishment of the Republic of Cyprus in 1960, the Squadron moved from Kermia to Dhekelia in the Sovereign Base Area.

653 Squadron is currently part of 3 Regiment Army Air Corps, British Army of the Rhine.

Aden and the Radfan

In 1961, British forces in the Protectorate of Aden were reinforced following an increase in rioting and communist-inspired anti-government activity. The Army Air Corps was naturally called in to support the reinforcements, in the shape of 653 Squadron AAC. Initially the squadron was based at Sheikh Othman, the RAF Khormaksar emergency landing ground.

Aden was new ground to 653 Squadron so they were required to undertake local theatre familiarization training with Chipmunk T 10, up-country flights with RAF Twin Pioneers and the operational equipment in the shape of the Auster AOP 9, the last of that long line of workhorses of army aviation. Before active flying could commence, the Squadron moved to Falaise Camp with the REME workshops and other necessary elements of a successful aviation enterprise.

During 1961, part of the Squadron was rushed to the Persian Gulf to support the police action in support of the Kuwaiti government and, on the 'home front', the first Beaver AL 1s arrived in theatre. The Beavers were used for liaison and artillery support tasks, with the continued support of the Auster AOP 9s.

During 1962, the Squadron was active supporting multi-service exercises, although it was still under limited terrorist action from hill tribesmen who would sometimes engage aircraft, in the air or on the ground, with sniper fire. Most of the operational flying was in support of the Federation government forces in remote areas where air support was essential.

By then helicopters were entering service with the Army Air Corps, having been used in Kenyan Mau-Mau troubles, and the Alouette II carried out desert and hot/high trials in Aden, demonstrating that it had a role to play. By 1963, the Royalist versus Republican conflict in nearby Yemen had spread to the Aden border and it was obvious that there would be conflict there too.

In April 1964, the infamous Radfan operations began and the Army

Above *The Beaver AL 1 was widely used after its introduction to Aden, carrying people and supplies (artillery shells in this case) to outposts which would have been impossible or too dangerous to have reached by road. (*Museum of Army Flying*)*

Below *A Beaver of 653 Squadron, Army Air Corps, overflying the jagged peaks of Little Aden in 1961. (*Major John Dicksee*)*

The Auster AOP 9 was a very versatile aircraft in army service, including its capability of landing on aircraft carrier flight decks; this is an Auster of 653 Squadron landing on Centaur *in 1961. (*Major John Dicksee)

Air Corps, still in the shape of 653 Squadron, provided the services of the remaining four Auster AOP 9, five Beaver AL 1s and two newly arrived Westland Scout AL 1 helicopters. The Scout was described as 'a status symbol and all recces (requested by ground units) had to be carried out by Scout', even when the Beaver could do the job as well, if not better.

Forward Air Control was provided by both Auster and Beaver, the tasking of the Scout depending on whether a remote site landing was required. With the development of the Special Air Service role in Aden's Radfan, the Scout came into its own in support of the 'Sabre' squadrons employed in the remote hill areas, carrying SAS teams into the mountains. Although small arms fire was met, it could be countered by return fire from the troops inside the helicopter or by supporting 105 mm artillery fire.

In the Radfan, the helicopter demonstrated to the British Army that helicopters could be used for offensive air operations in support of ground forces but also that they were vulnerable even to small arms fire. In the Radfan mountains, the heat and altitude restrictions on the helicopter meant that the payload was necessarily reduced.

The Army Air Corps learned a great deal about the operation of helicopters in these hostile, mountainous conditions, not just from the pure aviation point of view, but also how to achieve a safe landing and take-off in an area of enemy activity. In terms of operational practicalities, the Scout and Beaver aircraft were moved up from Aden itself to the Radfan area to directly support the troops on the ground and to 'get to know' the people who mattered — those being directly supported. The Radfan operation, more precisely the recapture of Jebel Windina, led to the first Army Air Corps night assault operation, also carried out by Scout.

Of the lessons learned during that campaign, amongst the most important was the fact that the helicopter's presence is a good morale-booster for the troops on the ground, especially because of its ability to recover casualties from otherwise inaccessible locations, and also that helicopters must be employed as part of the overall combat team. The Scout helicopter achieved considerable fame in Aden, having been committed to operations under enemy fire just four weeks after arriving in the Middle East.

The end of the Radfan operations in September 1964 saw the end of the Auster in the Middle East, it also saw the introduction of the Sioux light observation helicopter and an increase in urban terrorist activity in Aden proper. The Army Air Corps presence was increased so that the mountainous areas of Southern Arabia could be watched and the terrorism in Aden contained. Amongst the new arrivals to the army flying scene at that time was the Westland-built Sioux which served until the UK withdrawal in 1967.

*After the withdrawal from Aden, army aviation remained in several Middle Eastern locations including Sharjah. This 13 Flight AAC Scout is receiving attention from 74 Aircraft Workshop REME. (*R O Parr)

Borneo

When Indonesia achieved independence from the Netherlands in 1949, the newly-installed President Sukarno determined to bring Malaya, Singapore, Brunei and the other islands into the Indonesian federation. In 1963, Indonesia decided to 'confront' Malaysia and other nations in the area and so began Confrontation.

Like the Malayan Peninsula, Borneo island is almost totally jungle, with rivers used by the native people as the only means of transportation. The border with Indonesian Kalimantan was not marked and patrols had to be made along its length following Indonesian incursions.

Support was given to the troops on the ground by Wessex helicopters of the Royal Navy and the light helicopters and aircraft of several air troops and flights. Sioux, Scout and Auster aircraft were used in this short but highly effective campaign.

Unlike the Malayan Emergency mentioned earlier, Confrontation was a fluid, fast-moving series of actions which demonstrated that joint helicopter warfare was possible; 'Give 100 men some helicopters and they will do the job of a thousand,' said the British Director of Operations, General Sir Walter Walker, after the 1966 peace treaty had been signed. He based his army light helicopters forward to support troops on the ground and insisted that air force and naval helicopters were similarly available to the brigade commanders.

Borneo proved a testing area for the British Army's helicopter forces, operating aircraft like this Sioux AH 1; note the survival pack on the skid. (Robin Adshead)

Above *During the Confrontation with Indonesia, the British Army operated the Auster AOP 9 and the Sioux AH 1 in support of ground forces. (*Robin Adshead)

Below *In the hot and humid conditions in Borneo, Army Air Corps Scout helicopters had doors and unnecessary fittings removed to save weight. (*Robin Adshead)

The Falklands campaign

'Without our light helicopters and their gallant air crew many young men alive today would be dead, many of our attacks would have foundered for lack of ammunition and the campaign would have taken longer to win ... They really were the bravest of anyone.' — Major General Julian Thompson CB, OBE, ADC writing in the *Army Air Corps Journal*, 1983

The story of the role of the light helicopter in the Falklands during April, May and June 1982 is one of skill, courage and determination. It is the story of the combined resources of the Army Air Corps, the 3rd Commando Brigade Air Squadron Royal Marines, the Royal Electrical and Mechanical Engineers, the Royal Signals and the Royal Army Ordnance Corps. Helicopters were provided to the British amphibious task force by 656 Squadron, Army Air Corps (normally attached to 1st Infantry Brigade) but chosen to support 5th Infantry ('Out of Area') Brigade because of a close working relationship with 2nd Battalion The Parachute Regiment. The 656 Squadron was equipped with six Gazelle AH 1, some of which were fitted with SNEB freeflight rocket pods, and six SS. 11 capable Scout AH 1 helicopters. The Gazelles and Scouts were fitted for, but not necessarily with, overwater flotation gear.

For the majority, the campaign to regain the Falkland Islands began on 1 April 1982, just after 3rd Commando Brigade had returned from annual winter training in Norway. Most of the air crew and technicians

had, in fact, departed to take leave, yet within hours of the call to duty two-thirds were ready to join the Task Force. In addition to the Royal Marines Gazelle and Scout helicopters, three Scouts from 656 Squadron AAC were placed under command for the journey south.

Immediately after the landings at San Carlos on 21 May 1982, Sea King helicopters of the Royal Navy were used to transfer men and equipment to outlying hills to protect them against air attack. During an escort tasking for the naval Sea Kings, the light helicopter force suffered its first losses — two RM Gazelles were shot down by small arms fire, killing three and wounding a fourth air crew member. A third Gazelle was badly damaged but returned to RFA *Sir Galahad.* Nevertheless, operations continued unabated, preparing for the forthcoming breakout towards Darwin and Goose Green.

Within days of arriving in the Falkland Islands, the 656 Squadron advance party commander, Captain John Greenhalgh (a Royal Corps of Transport officer serving with the Army Air Corps) won the Distinguished Flying Cross for casualty evacuation of the injured whilst under fire and in complete darkness. These casualty evacuations (known as casevacs) were extremely hazardous operations due to a number of threats including marauding Argentine Pucara ground attack aircraft, two of which engaged a pair of Scouts, destroying one and damaging the other in a twisting, turning fight at very low altitude.

The Battle of Goose Green opened the way for the assault on Port Stanley as British forces were reinforced by additional units of 5

Left *Army Air Corps Gazelle AH 1 helicopters of 656 Squadron were fitted with the 68 mm SNEB rocket launcher during light helicopter operations in the South Atlantic; this example, seen at Middle Wallop at the 1982 Air Day, is also fitted with the Ferranti observation aid in the cabin roof.*

Right *Retaining its guided missile outriggers, this Scout AH 1 is pictured during underslung load operations in support of the British forces which liberated the Falklands in 1982. (*British Army / UKLF*)*

Captain John Greenhalgh DFC (right) and Sergeant John Gammon hold the painting, commissioned by Ferranti Instrumentation, which shows their missile attack on an Argentine artillery position during the Falklands conflict. The photograph was taken at the Museum of Army Flying, Middle Wallop.

Infantry Brigade, including the remaining aircraft from 656 Squadron. The Scouts which arrived were armed with SS.11 missiles, which were allocated to provide a mobile attack force in case British troops met armoured vehicles; in the event the missiles were used against strongpoints and artillery rather than armour.

The AAC and RM air crew and their support technicians had to familiarize themselves with an inhospitable terrain in the Falklands, devoid of the cover of trees which light helicopters use to survive in other parts of the world. The two breakout lines — north past Teal Inlet or south via Bluff Cove — were equally bad country for light helicopters, but the joint light helicopter force operated in all the locations. Clandestine operations as well as regular resupply missions inbound and casualty evacuation outbound were undertaken day or night.

The fight for Port Stanley included another heroic casevac under fire when Captain Sam Drennan gained another DFC for the Army Air Corps by undertaking a very hazardous mission to Mount Tumbledown to lift out wounded Scots Guardsmen. After the fighting, Captain Jeff Niblett and the late Captain Richard Nunn, both Royal Marines, were also awarded the Distinguished Flying Cross, the Military Cross going to Major Peter Cameron, OC 3 Cdo Bde Air Sqn and the Distinguished Flying Medal to Sergeant W. C. O'Brien, Royal Marines. Between them, the light helicopter force won some 35 awards for their part in the campaign — a considerable number indicating the vital role played by the helicopter.

Significant dates

1918	Royal Flying Corps merged into Royal Air Force
1934	Royal Artillery Flying Club formed
1939	Artillery spotting trials at Larkhill
1940	First glider trials
1941	First Air Observation Post unit formed (651 Squadron)
1942	Original Army Air Corps formed (Glider Pilot Regiment and Parachute Regiment — later followed by the Special Air Service)
1942–45	Distinguished war service by Air OPs
1943	First use of British gliders during Sicily landings
1944	British gliders highly successful at D-Day landings
1944	Operation Market Garden at Arnhem
1946–47	First helicopter trials
1950	Army Air Corps disbanded
1951–53	Air OPs in Korea
1955	Joint Experimental Helicopter Unit formed
1956	World's first heliborne assault at Suez
1957	First production Skeeter flown
	Re-formation of the Army Air Corps from Air OP squadrons and Light Liaison Flights
	Glider Pilot Regiment disbanded
	Permanent cadre of pilots established
1958	Middle Wallop handed over to the AAC
1960	Westland Scout ordered
1961	Alouette AH 2 enters service
1967	Guided weapon trials
1968	Formation of Blue Eagles team
1969–70	AAC Regiments formed
1972	Helicopter anti-tank trials
1973	Permanent AAC cadre extended to ground crew
1982	Operation Corporate in the Falkland Islands
1982	Silver Jubilee celebrations
1986	First Reserve helicopter squadron formed
1987	Two-pilot crewing of helicopters
1995	Light attack helicopter to be introduced

STRUCTURE AND COMMAND ARRANGEMENTS

The Present Force

Britain's Army Air Corps is comprised of some 300 helicopters and fixed-wing aircraft, operated by some 2,800 officers and men, making up about two per cent of the British Army's current manpower. In budgetary terms, the equipment represents nearly six per cent of British Army spending but in terms of man to airframe ratio, the Army Air Corps is one of the most economical forces anywhere in the world, with a 10:1 ratio.

Today's Army Air Corps has a permanent cadre of officers and men 'cap badged' with the famous sky blue beret and silver eagle emblem, but it is significant that a continuing, albeit reducing, proportion of officers and senior non-commissioned officers (NCOs) are attached for duty from other Corps and Regiments of the British Army. This ensures a wide variety of experience, part of which is continually changing.

On the battlefield the modern helicopter, although one of the four direct fire arms, cannot operate autonomously and is part of an all-arms force which also includes the infantry, armoured and artillery, as well as the supporting services.

Any military organization requires adequate command, control and communications (C3) arrangements in order to function correctly. In

The leading edge of today's Army Air Corps is the Westland Lynx AH 1 helicopter, armed with the Hughes Aircraft Company's TOW anti-tank missile system which is guided by the British Aerospace TOW roof sight. (BAe)

The British Army has several important NATO commitments outside BAOR, including the provision of light helicopters, such as this Gazelle AH 1, to AMF for Arctic operations. (British Army/UKLF)

In Hong Kong, the Army Air Corps has an independent squadron of Scout AH 1 helicopters, with a detached flight in Brunei. One of the Scouts is pictured here working with two Bell 212 helicopters of the Sultan's defence forces. (British Army/ 660 Squadron)

The Army Air Corps assists Royal Marines' light helicopter support by providing equipment like these Gazelles and in pilot and aircrewman training. (Bob Downey)

the United Kingdom, the British Army, together with the Royal Navy and the Royal Air Force, is no longer concerned solely with the protection of the country and its colonies, but also with the protection of peace in Europe and other parts of the world under international or bi-national treaty obligations.

To support the British Army in NATO (North Atlantic Treaty Organization) areas, Hong Kong, the Falkland Islands (until 31 May 1987), Cyprus and Belize, the Army Air Corps maintains an effective C3 organization to administer, support and control helicopters and a limited number of fixed-wing aircraft world-wide. As part of the United Kingdom's current defence policy is the support of Out of Area operations, the Army Air Corps has to be capable of operating in all climates and all conditions. This was demonstrated in 1982 when 656 Squadron AAC was deployed to the Falkland Islands in support of 5 Infantry Brigade, together with 3 Commando Brigade Air Squadron, Royal Marines. The primary function, however, remains the aviation support of British Army of the Rhine (BAOR), part of NATO's central front in Federal Germany.

Director Army Air Corps

The Director Army Air Corps has his Headquarters (known as the Directorate) at the former Battle of Britain airfield at Middle Wallop in Hampshire. He is the functional head of the Corps and although he is

Gazelle load lifting during an exercise to move fuel using the Bridport Aviation nets. (Patrick Allen)

Scout helicopters of the Territorial Army-manned 666 Squadron at Netheravon.

Above *Auster AOP 9 over the jungle of Sarawak during the Confrontation period. (*Colonel John Everett-Heath*)*

Below *Scout AH 1 at Kluang during operations in Borneo in 1967; the helicopter is painted dark earth/green and marked with day-glo panels to aid identification in the event of a jungle force landing. (*R O Parr*)*

*The former wartime officers' mess of RAF Middle Wallop, this building now houses the staff of the Director Army Air Corps. (*AACC)

not on operational commander in his own right he has responsibility for:

a administration of the 'Regiment';
b advice on the provision of aviation support to Commander British Army of the Rhine (BAOR);
c advice on the provision of aviation support to Commander United Kingdom Land Forces (UKLF);
d advice on the provision of aviation support to Major General Royal Marines (CGRM). The Royal Marines air squadron is equipped with standard army helicopters and the majority of the aircrew are trained with the Army Air Corps;
e future policy and equipment for the Army Air Corps;
f Army Air Corps manpower and personnel.

British Army of the Rhine (BAOR)

BAOR consists of some 55,000 men, with several garrisons, and has its main combat echelon in 1st (British) Corps which itself consists of three Armoured Divisions (1st, 3rd and 4th) with an Infantry Division completing the defence strike force.

To support the armoured divisions in their primary role of defending the Inner German Border (IGB) between the Federal Republic of Germany (West) and its communist neighbour the Democratic Republic of Germany (East), Commander 1 (BR) Corps has three

regiments of Army Air Corps helicopters, together with an Army Air Corps support squadron. Each regiment consists of three helicopter squadrons and a Headquarters squadron.

The aviation commander is an Army Air Corps Brigadier, based at the Corps headquarters in Bielefield; his title is Commander Aviation, British Army of the Rhine. Since 1986, his duties have included the support of British Army training operations in Canada with the British Army Training Unit Suffield (BATUS) on the prairies of Alberta.

Aviation support for Northern Ireland calls for air crew and aircraft engineers to be drawn from BAOR units and, in the past, units also served tours in the Falkland Islands.

The Army Air Corps units in BAOR are equipped with the Westland-built Aerospatiale SA 341 Gazelle light observation and liaison helicopter and the Westland Lynx AH 1, armed with the Hughes Aircraft Corporation TOW wire and optically-guided anti-tank missile. From 1988, the improved Lynx AH 7 will be delivered to BAOR at the start of a replacement and updating programme.

United Kingdom Land Forces (UKLF)

The other aviation commander is Commander Aviation, United Kingdom Land Forces, based at Netheravon airfield in Wiltshire, close to the UKLF headquarters at Wilton. In addition to support within the United Kingdom, he is required to plan the support and resource management of helicopter units in the Far East (Hong Kong and Brunei), the Mediterranean (Cyprus) and Central America (Belize). Included in this task is that of supplying aviation support for exercises overseas, including Canada, Norway, Kenya and anywhere else that the British Army may train.

Left *Although primarily used in the anti-tank role, the Lynx is easily adapted to the troop carrying role and can deploy an infantry section.* (Rolls-Royce/Peter Scott)

Right *United Kingdom Land Forces has the support of both Gazelle (left) and Lynx (right) for a variety of roles, including specialist trooping and liaison.* (Patrick Allen)

Although heavily centralized, this form of management has proved to be more cost-effective, and better in military terms, than having individual aviation commanders around the world. Besides the small planning staff at Netheravon there is an inspection cell which operates around the world checking on flying and engineering standards. In peacetime, Commander Aviation (Comd Avn) UKLF has to ensure the fitness for role of a number of disparate units.

UKLF control of helicopter assets includes an independent squadron in Hong Kong. (British Army/UKLF)

Unit organization

Since the Army Air Corps's formation in 1957, there have been several major changes in the functional organization of the Corps and today the structure is based on three levels of command; regiment, squadron and flight.

The regiment Command is held by the Commanding Officer, a Lieutenant Colonel, with a Major as Second-in-Command; both are flying posts, but in wartime these officers are more likely to be giving aviation advice and commanding operations for the Divisional commanders.

The squadron The squadron is the basic operational unit of the Army Air Corps and consists of between twelve and eighteen helicopters, twelve Westland Lynx AH 1/7 and six Aerospatiale Gazelle AH 1s for the BAOR units as an example. The officer commanding a squadron is a Major and for administrative reasons he will have the squadron divided into Flights. Supporting him is a Qualified Helicopter Instructor (QHI), generally a Warrant Officer or Staff Sergeant who is responsible for keeping flight safety standards. There are a number of independent squadrons operating outside the regimental system, such as 660 Squadron in Hong Kong.

The flight The smallest administrative unit in the Army Air Corps is the Flight. These can either be integral to the squadrons or are independent in their own right, such as 12 Flight in British Army of the Rhine. There are also independent Flights working in Out of Area locations such as Belize and Cyprus. These independent Flights are also commanded by a Major.

The Flight: 7 Flt AAC at Berlin's Gatow airfield. Flanking the all ranks group are two of the Flight's Gazelle AH 1 helicopters. (British Army / 7 Flight)

The smallest engineering support unit is the REME Light Aid Detachment which takes care of first line maintenance. (British Army / 7 Flight)

The REME and Army Flying

The Royal Electrical and Mechanical Engineers (REME) provide the engineering back-up in the field to the Army Air Corps throughout the world to keep the Corps's equipment operational. A special relationship has developed between the REME and AAC over the years.

Field Maintenance

Light Aid Detachment (LAD) This is the smallest REME unit which supports operational units in the field with first line maintenance. For example in British Army of the Rhine, LADs are found at Flight and squadron levels.

Aircraft Workshop (Ac Wksp) There are both Regimental

In 1983, 70 Aircraft Workshop, REME, received a unique commendation for its role in Operation Corporate, being the only complete unit to be so honoured. 70 Ac Wksp provided Aircraft Maintenance Groups for 656 Squadron AAC and 3rd Commando Brigade Air Squadron, Royal Marines, as well as base support in the United Kingdom. (British Army / SW District)

Workshops and Aircraft Workshops, the latter being an independent unit commanded by a Lieutenant Colonel whilst the former are commanded by a Major, but under command of the parent Army Air Corps Regiment to which they belong. The implication of a Regimental Workshop is that it can carry out second line repairs, although the Aircraft Workshop remains the main unit for these tasks.

Aircraft Maintenance Group (AMG) These are part of an Aircraft Workshop, but Groups are assigned to an Army Air Corps Regiment in time of tension or war, joining the unit in the field.

Deep maintenance Aircraft requiring deep maintenance, including major modifications, are normally sent to the United Kingdom's main tri-service helicopter facility at Royal Naval Aircraft Yard at Fleetlands, near Portsmouth. In addition, the Royal Navy provides specialist helicopter engineers and the MARTSU (Mobile Aircraft Repair, Transport and Salvage Unit) teams to recover aircraft damaged by flying accidents or in wartime, but which cannot be brought back to Fleetlands.

Battle Damage Repair (BDR) Although the basic principles are the same for all aircraft — returning a valuable asset to the field in the shortest possible time, using the safest yet quicket techniques — the British Army has developed its own helicopter procedures in the light of conflict, and these were proven during the Falklands campaign. It has been said that a fair proportion of light helicopters in that conflict would have been considered non-operational without the application

Left *In the field maintenance during Exercise Lionheart. An NBC-clad technician of the REME works on the Rolls-Royce Gem engine from a Lynx AH 1 helicopter in make-shift conditions in a German farmer's barn. (*Rolls-Royce*)*

Right *Battle damage repair was an art quickly re-learned in the Falklands, where it proved vital for keeping the light helicopters airborne; two technicians work on a Gazelle canopy in this picture. (*Bob Downey*)*

of BDR and field maintenance procedures. It is stressed that BDR can only be used to its fullest extent after peacetime flying rules have been lifted.

Spares supply The REME is supported at all times by the Royal Army Ordnance Corps (RAOC) for spares supply and specialist weapons work. The main support is provided at unit level by ready-use stocks of spares and some RAOC personnel, with further and much more extensive stocks being held in specialist RAOC units co-located with the REME aircraft workshops. At Middle Wallop, the RAOC has deployed 1 Aircraft Support Unit (1 Ac Sp Unit) and in British Army of the Rhine there is 2 Ac Sp Unit, RAOC.

SAS and army flying

Always linked with army flying and the Army Air Corps, the Special Air Service (SAS) regiment was part of the original Army Air Corps which was disbanded on 22 May 1950, with the SAS becoming a separate regiment in its own right.

Recently, with international coverage of the Iranian Embassy seige and the Falklands special operations, the role of the helicopter in SAS operations has again come into public focus. For very good reasons, the *modus operandi* of the Special Air Service is kept particularly secret and little is officially said about the regiment and its role.

From articles in the public domain, especially from the Fleet Street press, it is possible to conclude that the SAS is particularly well trained

It is thought that the Special Air Service makes use of the captured Argentine Army Agusta A109 helicopters from the Falklands conflict; it is inevitable that other types would also be used.

in use of helicopters. In 1983–84 there was particular comment about the use of Italian-built Agusta A109 helicopters being acquired to support the SAS, and whilst this has not been officially confirmed neither has it been denied. SAS helicopter support is not wholly the province of the Army Air Corps, although some members of the Corps are thought to have served with the regiment.

Northern Ireland

Although there have been helicopters with the resident garrisons in Northern Ireland since the beginning of rotary-wing army aviation, it has only been since the current spate of 'troubles' began in 1969 that there has been a signficiant increase in the presence of the Army Air Corps in the Province. For obvious security reasons it is not possible to go into great detail about the role, tasks, organizations and effectiveness of the Gazelle, Lynx and Beaver operations in Northern Ireland, but the following information has been made available for publication.

The Northern Ireland Regiment, commanded by a Lieutenant Colonel, is made up of two helicopter squadrons and a fixed-wing Flight with main bases at Aldergrove and Ballykelly. There are also a number of out stations, including Bessbrook Mill and Omagh, from where quick reaction operations are mounted.

The NI Regiment reports to the General Officer Commanding Northern Ireland (GOC NI) for tasking and operations, but his main aviation advice comes from Commander Aviation, United Kingdom Land Forces. The two helicopter squadrons and the fixed-wing Flight support the regular operations of the Royal Ulster Constabulary, the British Army and the Ulster Defence Regiment for peacekeeping operations. With the decrease in the number of troops on the streets,

44

British Army helicopters in Northern Ireland are unarmed and often operate in non-military roles, such as assisting a local aviation museum with the transportation of a Wildcat naval fighter wreck from Lough Foyle.

there has been an increase in the number of helicopter sorties.

In recent years the operational basis for the Army Air Corps activities in Northern Ireland has changed, with a greater proportion of personnel being resident for two years in the Province rather than coming from United Kingdom Land Forces and British Army of the Rhine units on emergency tours as used to be the case. It is perhaps surprising to note that a number of air crew want to extend their tours after a posting to Northern Ireland, because in the words of one Sergeant 'It's actually doing a job for somebody, and although the work is not predictable, you get real satisfaction from the flying'.

Helicopter operations are jointly tasked by the Air Support Operations Centre, manned by both Army Air Corps and RAF personnel and responsible for assigning the best available helicopter assets to the ground units making bids or for supplying emergency cover for an incident. The introduction of the Lynx, replacing the Scout, has been especially important because of the former's better capabilities with bad weather, payload and range.

REGIMENTS, SQUADRONS AND THE AAC CENTRE

1 Regiment AAC

The Regiment, which provides anti-tank support for the 1st Armoured Division, is based at Hildensheim, some 35 km (22 miles) from the Inner German Border separating East and West Germany. It is a former Luftwaffe home defence air station shared a Royal Tank Regiment unit and a major Bundeswehr (Federal German Armed Forces) reserve ambulance unit. 1 Regiment consists of a Headquarters squadron and three anti-tank helicopter squadrons (651, 652 and 661 Sqns), with a mix of Lynx AH 1 and Gazelle AH 1 helicopters.

In Federal Germany, the Army Air Corps directly supports the Armoured Divisions of the British Army of the Rhine and other units; Gazelle and Chieftain tank working together.

1 Regiment, Army Air Corps, is based close to the Inner German Border and is equipped with Lynx and Gazelle (illustrated) helicopters. (British Army / 1 Armoured Div)

3 Regiment AAC

Home for this Regiment is the former Canadian base at Soest. The Regiment provides anti-tank support to 3rd Armoured Division and for the neighbouring 1st (Belgian) Corps which is without any armed helicopter support of its own. 3 Regt AAC consists of Headquarters squadron and three anti-tank squadrons (653, 662 and 663 Sqns) with a mix of Gazelle AH 1 and Lynx AH 1 helicopters.

4 Regiment AAC

4 Regiment provides anti-tank support to 4th Armoured Division and is based at Detmold, again on an old Luftwaffe airfield. The Regiment consists of Headquarters squadron and three anti-tank squadrons (654, 659 and 669 Sqns), again with a mix of Lynx AH 1 and Gazelle AH 1 helicopters.

7 Regiment AAC

This unit has its headquarters at Netheravon on Salisbury Plain, close to the United Kingdom Land Forces headquarters at Wilton. It is a unique organization providing squadrons and Flights for a multitude of

Part of 7 Regiment's remit is the deployment of helicopters to the NATO flanks, as here in Norway during winter training exercises. (Rolls-Royce)

different functions in many different parts of Great Britain and other parts of the World. 7 Regiment currently consists of three squadrons (656, 658 and 666 (V) Sqns) and three autonomous Flights (2, 3 and 8 Flts). The roles of these units are many and varied but cover the two major areas of reinforcement to NATO and Home Defence of the United Kingdom. The Regiment also may deploy detachments for exercises overseas.

Northern Ireland Regiment

The Army Air Corps has played an important part in the support for the civil power given in Ulster by the British Army. Today there are two mixed squadrons of Lynx and Gazelle (655 and 665 Sqns) together with a flight of Beaver aircraft for border patrol and communication tasks. All British Army aircraft operating in Northern Ireland are unarmed.

Falkland Islands Squadron

This unit was disbanded following the scaling down of British forces in the Islands and it withdrew completely on 31 May 1987.

657 Squadron AAC

With twelve helicopters, split evenly between Lynx AH 1 and Gazelle AH 1, the Squadron is based at Oakington (Cambridgeshire) and has a British Army of the Rhine reinforcement role in wartime.

Following the Falklands conflict, the Army Air Corps supplied light helicopter support to the garrison, initially with Lynx and Gazelle, later replacing the Lynx with Scout. The deployment was completed in May 1987. (British Army/FI)

660 Squadron AAC

Based at Sek Kong in Hong Kong's new territories, 660 Sqn provides the commander of the British forces and the Gurkha Brigade with light aviation support in the internal security and civil assistance roles. Because Hong Kong is such a small place, the aviation assets of the

Chinese children are shown around a Scout AH 1 from 660 Squadron by Corporal M Coleman during the Sek Kong Community Relations Day in 1986. (JSPRS)

660 Squadron is co-located with an RAF Support Helicopter squadron at Sek Kong in Hong Kong's New Territories.

British Army, Royal Air force and Royal Hong Kong Auxiliary Air Force are integrated through a centralized tasking system. Flying the Westland Scout AH 1, 660 Sqn detaches a flight to support the Gurkha Battalion based in Brunei, an independent kingdom on the island of Borneo, with which the UK has a defence agreement. In addition, the helicopters support British Army and Royal Marines jungle training in Brunei.

During joint-service exercises in Hong Kong, a Scout is refuelled from a cache of 45 Imp gal drums 'in the field'. (JSPRS)

664 Squadron AAC

This special unit of twelve Gazelle AH 1 helicopters is charged with forward reconnaissance and as Corps communications aircraft for 1 (BR) Corps. Much of the exercising by the squadron is in support of ground-based reconnaissance units. Based at Minden, where new hangar facilities were completed in late 1986, the unit also has a role supporting the British Frontier Service (BFS).

BFS is a unique organization which patrols the Inner German Border (IGB) in the former British sector of Germany. In this task, the Service is supported by helicopters of 664 Squadron, the only British aviation unit allowed to approach this part of the IGB and only allowed to fly the actual boundary line with a BFS officer aboard. The reconnaissance operations are performed unarmed and only in order to assess any changes in the policing of the IGB by the East German and other Warsaw Pact forces.

666 Squadron AAC (V)

Formed on 26 April 1986, the British Army's first helicopter squadron manned by the Territorial Army is also the first operational squadron to be manned by civilians for almost thirty years. To carry out its role of supporting UKLF and Territorial Army units, the squadron is equipped with twelve Scout helicopters and an establishment strength of 43, including eighteen pilots. Each pilot has at least 3,000 flying hours. The helicopters, based at Netheravon, are not armed.

In wartime, 666 Squadron would be operating with UKLF for Home Defence tasks and this is where the unit differs from the Territorial Army Pool of Pilots (mainly employed in the British commercial helicopter industry) which has a war role of reinforcing BAOR units.

7 Flight AAC

Operating from RAF Gatow in Berlin, this small flight of three Gazelles and four pilots is allocated to the Berlin Brigade, directly under the control of the Brigade Headquarters but being tasked by any authorized agency. The Flight's main roles are surveillance of the Berlin Wall, VIP and other personnel movements, law enforcement in support of the Berlin Police, assisting the fire brigade, customs service and river police.

12 Flight AAC

Based at RAF Wildenrath, this is the Headquarters British Army of the Rhine and senior officer transportation unit and on any one day its helicopters can be seen in many parts of the Federal German Republic and even as far afield as the NATO headquarters in Belgium.

Left *Permanent features of the Berlin-based 7 Flt AAC Gazelle helicopters are the Nightsun light boom and the Union Flag marking. (British Army)* •

Below *A Gazelle of 12 Flight AAC at RAF Wildenrath; note the RAF Phantoms on the taxiway below. (RAFG)*

Bottom *16 Flight AAC at Dhekelia, Cyprus, continued to fly the 25-year-old Alouette AH 2 during 1987. (David Oliver)*

Based at Belize Airport, 25 Flight AAC is an 'out of area' unit administered by UKLF. (David Oliver)

16 Flight AAC

Based in Cyprus, 16 Flt is one of only two units still flying the Alouette II. The Flight is likely to be re-equipped with the Gazelle AH 1 helicopter in the near future, since the Alouette becomes more expensive to maintain as its age increases. The unit undertakes support of the Sovereign Base Area, training for hot and high flying and is a welcome posting for most pilots, the attractions of the island being obvious.

25 Flight AAC

Most pilots and ground crew spend only four months in Belize when attached to 25 Flight, except the permanent HQ cadre where the Officer Commanding is usually a senior Major with an instructor's qualification. The role of the Flight's Gazelles, based at Airport Camp, Belize City, is to support army and other units in protecting the sovereignty of the independent Commonwealth state in troubled Central America. The Flight is equipped with Gazelle AH 1 helicopters and much of the flying is over jungle or similarly inhospitable terrain.

BATUS Flight AAC

Operating from Suffield in the Canadian province of Alberta, the BATUS Flight is now only equipped with Gazelle AH 1 helicopters since the last Beaver was returned to the United Kingdom in 1984. The role of the Flight is to provide helicopter support for the armoured

A Gazelle AH 1 from the BATUS Flight over the open country of the Suffield ranges. (AACC)

and other British Army units undertaking battle group training on the wide Canadian prairies.

UN Flight AAC

Supporting the United Nations forces on Cyprus from its base at Nicosia International Airport, the Flight (like 16 Flt) is equipped with the Alouette II, but is in support of the multi-national force for buffer zone reconnaissance.

Supporting the United Nations forces from Nicosia is an Army Air Corps flight with Alouette AH 2, to be replaced by the Gazelle by 1989. (David Oliver)

One of several Gazelle AH 1s used for pilot training at Middle Wallop.

Army Air Corps Centre

The home of the Army Air Corps is undoubtedly Middle Wallop, a grass airfield between Andover and Stockbridge on the edge of the Salisbury Plain in west Hampshire. It is a part of southern England which is close to the major military centres, such as Aldershot, Wilton, Bovington and Tidworth, as well as being less than an hour's flying time from London — by army helicopter.

Middle Wallop's history goes back to the Second World War when it was a Battle of Britain fighter station and then a night fighter base for the defence of the United Kingdom. Later it became an American base and hosted a Fleet Air Arm presence, before becoming the Royal Air Force's light aircraft centre. The first helicopters arrived in 1955 for the Joint Experimental Helicopter Unit and in 1957 it was transferred to RAF Home Command in preparation for the creation of the Army Air Corps Centre (AACC) in the September of that year. Royal Air Force aircraft technicians remained at Middle Wallop to support the new Corps until the Royal Electrical and Mechanical Engineers (REME) completed aircraft trade training. The station was actually handed over to army control on 1 October 1958.

The initial organization ran along RAF lines, including the adoption of the Pilot Training Wing (from 1965 called Flying Wing), Tactics Wing and Technical Wing. The AACC was the centre of all army aviation, with responsibility for the entire fleet until the creation of a headquarters for the Director Army Air Corps (HQ DAAC) in 1970 when the Centre's Commandant's rank changed from Brigadier to Colonel.

Taken in the late 1970s, this picture shows a Gazelle AH 1 overflying parked Sioux helicopters at Middle Wallop, the Army Air Corps Centre.

Prior to 1970 he had been termed the Brigadier Army Air Corps; DAAC is a Major General by rank.

In August 1965 a School of Army Aviation was formed, incorporating the new Flying Wing, ground training elements of the Tactics Wing and the former trades school (now called the Aircraft Engineering Wing of the REME). To complete the reorganization, the Aircraft Servicing Branch retained its separate identity and the Technical Wing was disbanded. Middle Wallop thus became known as the Army Aviation Centre. The School of Army Aviation was relatively short lived and closed in March 1973, with the Commandant taking over control of all Wings.

In 1966, a major building programme was commenced, including the erection of an instructional block called Stockwell Hall, named in memory of a former Colonel Commandant. For the technical side, and reflecting increasing need for specialist work on helicopters, avionics bays were built. The adoption of helicopter-mounted weapons necessitated the expansion of air crew training to include air gunners.

Almost contiguous with the closure of the School of Army Aviation, the Land/Air Warfare Directorate in London was closed and as part

Pictured in front of the control tower at AACC Middle Wallop are members of the Army Air Corps Eagles display team, led in the 1986 season by Captain Tony Davies AAC. (AACC)

of a centralization plan, Middle Wallop again received the title of Army Air Corps Centre. Co-located with the AACC is the HQ DAAC (see page 32) which is the policy and functional centre for all army flying.

Today there are no Army Air Corps operational units based at Middle Wallop (although both 70 Aircraft Workshop REME and 1 Aircraft Support Unit RAOC are Field Army units) but the largest grass airfield in Europe is still extremely busy with basic flying training (Chipmunks), initial and advanced helicopter training (Gazelle), conversion and air crewman training (Scout and Lynx) and fixed-wing training (Beaver). For further requirements the Centre hosts the Development and Trials Unit, and looking into the past it is also the home of the Museum of Army Flying.

Army Air Corps Bases

Throughout the world where the British Army operates on a permanent basis, there are the aviation bases for helicopters and the remaining Beaver fixed-wing aircraft. Some locations are small and the units only have lodger status whereas in other places, especially

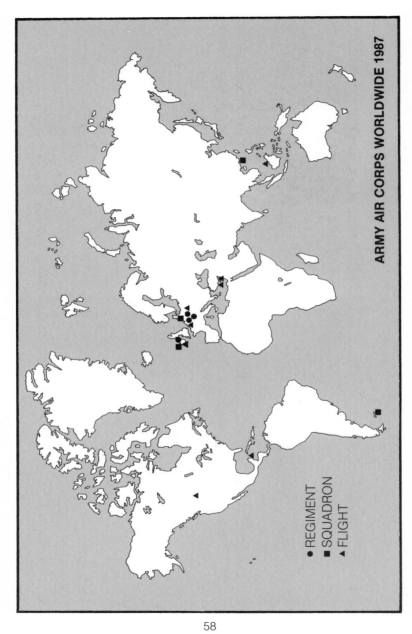

ARMY AIR CORPS WORLDWIDE 1987

● REGIMENT
■ SQUADRON
▲ FLIGHT

in British army of the Rhine, there are purpose-built facilities.

Aldergrove Co-located with Belfast International Airport and the Royal Air Force, the Army Air Corps presence at Aldergrove goes back many years but was extended when the 'troubles' began in 1969. Since then, Aldergrove has been the scene of almost continuous air operations by Beaver, Gazelle, Lynx, Scout and Sioux.

Ballykelly Situated near Londonderry, the former RAF airfield of Ballykelly houses several military units including a resident Army Air Corps squadron which looks after the police support role in western Ulster.

Belize The Army Air Corps detachment in Belize goes back to the early 1970s and the need to protect the interests of the then British colony of British Honduras which has since been granted independence, but which still requires the protection of the British Army and RAF. Today, a detachment of four Gazelles provides liaison, reconnaissance and communications flying for the garrison, including medical evacuation.

Berlin Co-located with RAF Gatow, the Berlin army aviation unit is 7 Flight which has three Gazelles for patrolling the British sector of the Berlin Wall and providing liaison for the Brigade commander at nearby Montgomery Barracks.

Bessbrook During the height of the 'troubles' in Northern Ireland,

Army Air Corps duties in Berlin include the daily patrol of the Berlin Wall by Gazelle; East Berlin's Communist party headquarters is in the background. (British Army)

Lynx helicopters used for advanced training at Middle Wallop.

this helipad was the busiest base in Europe, supporting operations in South Armagh and the border with the Irish Republic.

Detmold The main base of the Army Air Corps in Germany, it is now home to 4 Regiment AAC. It also houses the BAOR Lynx flight simulator.

Dhekelia This is the main army aviation facility in Cyprus, being in the Sovereign Base Area and supporting the Alouette II operations.

Falkland Islands Until May 1987 there was a squadron based in the Islands as part of the British Garrison, operating from Mount Pleasant Airport with small detachments across the islands daily to provide communications for the different military units present.

Hildesheim Headquarters of 1 Regiment AAC and nearest the Inner German Border, the airfield at Hildesheim is an old wartime fighter and training aerodrome.

Middle Wallop The home of the Army Air Corps, Middle Wallop is the Centre for flying training, trials, development and is the location of the Headquarters for the Director Army Air Corps.

Minden recently revamped with a new hangar facility, this small helicopter facility is home to 664 Squadron AAC.

Netheravon The home of the operational helicopter assigned to the United Kingdom Land Forces, situated on the edge of Salisbury

AAC UKLF LOCATIONS

BALLYKELLY
ALDERGROVE
TOPCLIFFE
OAKINGTON
NETHERAVON
MIDDLE WALLOP

Plain, not far from Wilton, UKLF's headquarters. It is also home to the only Territorial Army unit, 666 Squadron AAC (V).

Nicosia Home to the second Army Air Corps detachment in Cyprus, supporting the United Nations Force (UNFICYP).

Oakington Supporting the army units in East Anglia, the former RAF base near Cambridge was taken over by the Army Air Corps in the late 1970s.

Sek Kong The army aviation centre in Hong Kong, co-located with the RAF support helicopter facility. Sek Kong is in the New Territories and during the early 1980s was the scene of tremendous activity during the illegal immigration crisis. It is home to 660 Squadron AAC.

Soest The headquarters of 3 Regiment AAC, which supports 3rd Armoured Division of the British Army of the Rhine. In its time, it has also seen American and Canadian helicopter units, before being transferred to the Army Air Corps in the mid 1970s.

Suffield In Alberta, Canada is the home of the British Army Training Unit Suffield (BATUS) which now comes under the control of 1 (BR) Corps in Germany. Helicopters and fixed-wing aircraft are operated here in support of the battle group training exercises.

Topcliffe In Yorkshire is the base for army aviation supporting the units in the north of England. It is also an active RAF station.

Order of Battle 1986

British Army of the Rhine

Unit	Regiment	Base	Aircraft
651 Squadron	1 Regiment	Hildesheim	Lynx AH 1/Gazelle AH 1
652 Squadron	1 Regiment	Hildesheim	Lynx AH 1/Gazelle AH 1
653 Squadron	3 Regiment	Soest	Lynx AH 1/Gazelle AH 1
654 Squadron	4 Regiment	Detmold	Lynx AH 1/Gazelle AH 1
659 Squadron	4 Regiment	Detmold	Lynx AH 1/Gazelle AH 1
661 Squadron	1 Regiment	Hildesheim	Gazelle AH 1
662 Squadron	3 Regiment	Soest	Lynx AH 1/Gazelle AH 1
663 Squadron	3 Regiment	Soest	Lynx AH 1/Gazelle AH 1
664 Squadron	1 (BR) Corps	Minden	Gazelle AH 1
669 Squadron	4 Regiment	Detmold	Lynx AH 1/Gazelle AH 1
7 Flight	Garrison	Berlin	Gazelle AH 1
12 Flight	1 (BR) Corps	Wildenrath	Gazelle AH 1
BATUS Flight	BATUS	Suffield	Gazelle AH 1

United Kingdom Land Forces

656 Squadron	7 Regiment	Netheravon	Lynx AH 1/Gazelle AH 1
657 Squadron	19 Brigade	Oakington	Lynx AH 1/Gazelle AH 1
658 Squadron	7 Regiment	Netheravon	Gazelle AH 1/Scout AH 1

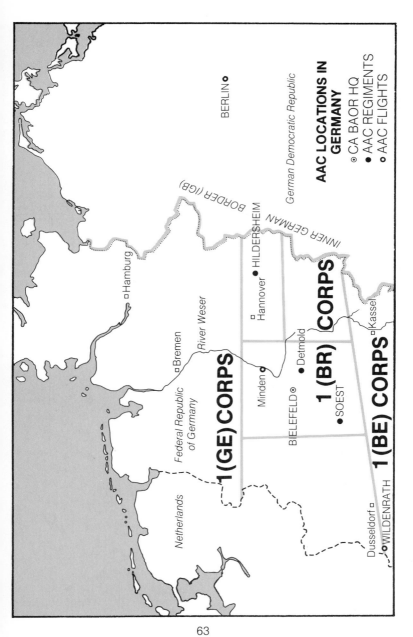

AAC LOCATIONS IN GERMANY

- ⊚ CA BAOR HQ
- ● AAC REGIMENTS
- ○ AAC FLIGHTS

BERLIN○

German Democratic Republic

BORDER (IGB)

INNER GERMAN

Federal Republic
of Germany

Netherlands

□ Hamburg

□ Bremen

River Weser

□ Hannover

● HILDERSHEIM

Minden ○

BIELEFELD⊚

● Detmold

□ Kassel

1(GE)CORPS

1(BR) CORPS

● SOEST

Dusseldorf □

○WILDENRATH

1(BE) CORPS

Unit	Regiment	Base	Aircraft
660 Squadron	HK Garrison	Sek Kong	Scout AH 1
666 Squadron	7 Regiment	Netheravon	Scout AH 1
2 Flight	7 Regiment	Netheravon	Gazelle AH 1
3 Flight	7 Regiment	Topcliffe	Gazelle AH 1
16 Flight	BF Cyprus	Dhekelia	Alouette AH 2
25 Flight	BF Belize	Belize	Gazelle AH 1
Det Flight	7 Regiment	Netheravon	Agusta A 109A
UN Flight	Garrison	Nicosia	Alouette AH 2

Northern Ireland

Unit	Regiment	Base	Aircraft
655 Squadron	NI Regiment	Ballykelly	Lynx AH 1 / Gazelle AH 1
665 Squadron	NI Regiment	Aldergrove	Lynx AH 1 / Gazelle AH 1
Beaver Flight	NI Regiment	Aldergrove	Beaver AL 1

Army Air Corps Centre

Chipmunk Squadron	Chipmunk T 10
Basic Rotary Squadron	Gazelle AH 1
Advanced Rotary Squadron	Gazelle AH 1
Operational Training Squadron	Gazelle AH 1 / Lynx AH 1 / Scout AH 1
Beaver Flight	Beaver AL 1
Demonstration & Trials Flight	Gazelle AH 1 / Lynx AH 1 / Scout AH 1
Historic Aircraft Flight	Sioux AH 1 / Skeeter AOP 10 / Auster AOP 9

AIRCRAFT

HELICOPTERS

Although helicopters have been a part of army flying since October 1946, when a few Sikorsky R4B aircraft were taken on strength for air observation post trials, the helicopter really did not come into its own with the Army Air Corps until the development of the Saunders-Roe Skeeter, originally designed by the Cierva Autogyro Company. Both companies later became absorbed in the Westland Aircraft Group, which is Britain's only helicopter designer and manufacturer today.

The Skeeter won a British Air Ministry requirement for an air observation post, to which role reconnaissance and liaison were later added. Two Skeeters were delivered for intensive trials in January 1957, and in September that year the Army Air Corps was formed. Three Skeeter AOP 10 and 64 Skeeter AOP 12 were built. Although not completely successful as a design, the Skeeter allowed the British Army its first taste of the capabilities of a light helicopter. To a certain extent, the Skeeter also showed limitations, some of which have remained in senior officers' minds until very recently.

Army pilots also flew helicopters of the Joint Helicopter Trials Units and often gained further experience with the Royal Navy and the Royal Air Force.

Development of the Skeeter was not directly possible, but a requirement was issued for a communications and liaison five-seat, turbine-powered helicopter, the Saunders Roe P 531 which eventually became the Westland Scout (see below). In the meantime, it was decided to purchase a number of Sud Aviation (now Aerospatiale) Alouette II helicopters which were of a comparable specification. The Alouette II also remains in service (see below).

The Skeeter was the Army Air Corps' first light helicopter.

Above *Diminutive but a useful first step, the Skeeter is remembered with great affection in the Army Air Corps. (*Westland*)*

Left *In the mid 1950s, the Joint Experimental Helicopter Unit was established at Middle Wallop and evaluated the Whirlwind for battlefield use. (*Museum of Army Flying*)*

Below left *Saunders-Roe (later part of Westland) developed the P 531 for the battlefield, initially with a wheeled undercarriage.*

Bottom left *After an international light helicopter competition, the British Army chose the Bell 47G to fulfil a light observation and training role. (*Westland*)*

**Agusta A 109A
Scale 1:72**

A slightly different version of the Sioux helicopter was purchased by Bristow Helicopters Ltd for an army training contract, the helicopter leaving Bristow's service in 1982.

Bell Model 47G was the other foreign type which was ordered for British Army service because of the delay in developing both the Scout and its Bristol Siddeley engine, eventually to become the Nimbus. In 1964, after flying off against Brantly and Hiller, the then War Office (later to become the Ministry of Defence) ordered the Bell 47G-3 variant, to be made under licence by Agusta of Italy and eventually by Westland at Yeovil, Somerset. The helicopter became known as the Sioux AH 1 and it first flew in March 1965. Having retired from service in 1976, it is still regarded with great affection by those who flew it. Bristow Helicopters operated the type under a civilian training contract for the Army Air Corps until 1982.

A 109

Agusta A 109A Hirundo: Purpose Utility and special transport; **Crew** 1/2 pilots; **Passengers** 6/7; **Maiden flight** 4 August 1971; **Service entry** 1983; **Range** 305 nm (565 km); **Max speed** 168 kt (311 km/h); **Cruising speed** 144 kt (267 km/h); **Service ceiling** 16,300 ft (4,970 m); **Hover In Ground Effect**

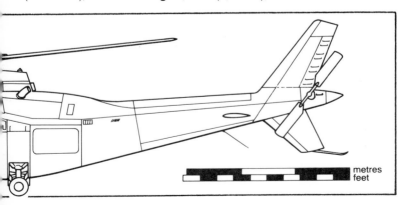

metres
feet

Agusta A 109A prior to adoption into Army Air Corps service.

9,800 ft (2,990 m); **Rate of climb** 1,620 ft/min (8.2 m/sec); **Length** 35.12 ft (10.7 m); **Height** 10.9 ft (3.3 m); **Rotor diameter** 36.1 ft (11 m); **Power plant** 2×Allison 250-C20B turbines (420 shp each); **All-up weight** 5,732 lb (2,600 kg); **Empty weight** 3,750 lb (1,701 kg); **Payload** 1,980 lb (898 kg); **Weapons** None.

The Agusta A 109 was developed as the first successful Italian helicopter project and four examples are operated by the Army Air Corps. Two of the helicopters were originally captured from the Argentine Army on the Falkland Islands and refurbished by Mann Aviation before being taken into the Army Air Corps' inventory. Later, two more of the type were purchased directly from the manufacturer in Milan.

The helicopters are operated for special transportation and liaison duties which, according to press reports, includes supporting the Special Air Service. It is British Army policy not to comment on the activities of the SAS and so this cannot be confirmed.

Alouette AH 2

Aerospatiale SE 3130B Alouette II: Purpose Utility and liaison; **Crew** 1 pilot, 1 aircrewman; **Passengers** 3/4; **Maiden flight** 12 March 1955; **Service evaluation** 1958–60; **Service entry** 1960; **Range** 162 nm (300 km); **Max speed** 100 kt (185 km/h); **Cruising speed** 90 kt (165 km/h); **Service ceiling** 7,385 ft))2,250 m); **Hover in Ground Effect** 5,400 ft (1,650 m); **Rate of climb** 925 ft/min (4.7 m/sec); **Length** 31.82 ft (9.7 m); **Height** 9 ft (2.74 m); **Rotor diameter** 33.46 ft (10.2 m); **Power plant** 1×Turbomeca Artouste II C6 turbine (360 shp); **All-up weight** 3,527 lb (1,600 kg); **Empty weight** 1,973 lb (895 kg); **Payload** 1,554 lb (705 kg); **Weapons** None.

The longest serving helicopter in today's Army Air Corps, the French-

Above *With red day-glo warning markings, this Gazelle AH 1 is from the Advanced Rotary Wing Flight at Middle Wallop.*

Below *Sioux AH 1 in United Nations markings during the helicopter's spell of duty in Cyprus.*

Above *Lynx HELARM goes under wires on the way to an exercise ambush in Germany.*

Below *Lynx HELARM using cover to move into position.*

Above *Marked for a NATO exercise, these Gazelles will be transporting umpires. (*Robin Adshead*)*

Below *Landing at Minden is the OC of 664 Squadron AAC, photographed from another Gazelle AH 1.*

Right *Alouette AH 2s were deployed to British Army of the Rhine.* (BAOR)

Left *An overwater rigged Gazelle based with 25 Flight AAC at Belize International Airport.* (David Oliver)

Below left *Gazelle AH 1 at Middle Wallop wearing the new light grey and green colour devised for British Army of the Rhine.*

Below *Twenty-five years on, the Alouette AH 2 continued to serve the British Army in Cyprus during 1987.* (British Army)

designed Alouette II or Lark was first adopted as a temporary measure until the Scout could be readied for service acceptance. Between 1960 and 1961, seventeen helicopters of the type were ordered, including two evaluation aircraft loaned to the British Army in 1958. It is destined to remain in service until 1995.

In the thirty years since its introduction, the helicopter has proved to

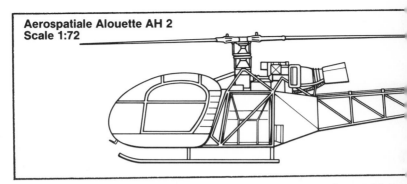

Aerospatiale Alouette AH 2
Scale 1:72

be perfect for the type of operations in Cyprus, operating at high altitude in hot conditions, supporting the United Nations forces (UNFICYP) and the British Sovereign Base Area. 16 Flight AAC's Alouettes have been deployed to Cyprus since 1964.

Army Air Corps records show that the Alouette has also been in operational service in British Guyana, Jamaica, Tanganyika / Zanzibar and Uganda as well as the more traditional operating area, the Federal Republic of Germany.

This extract is from the *Army Air Corps Journal,* author unknown: 'the Alouette (II) is easy to fly and once pilots adapt to the sensation, in the cruise, of sitting on a wooden chair with two large books under its back legs, flight becomes a great pleasure.'

Gazelle AH 1
Aerospatiale SA 341B Gazelle: Purpose Light observation, reconnaissance and liaison; **Crew** 1 pilot, 1 aircrewman; **Passengers** Up to 4; **Maiden**

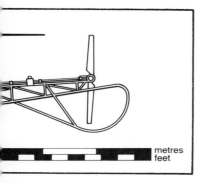

metres
feet

Below left *One of the helicopters jointly produced by Westland and Aerospatiale was the Gazelle AH 1. (Bob Downey)*

Below *Equally at home in the Arctic, the Gazelle has served the British Army in almost every place it has operated in the last ten years. (British Army/UKLF)*

flight 2 August 1968 (prototype), 31 January 1972 (SA 341B); **Service entry** 1973; **Range** 362 nm (670 km); **Max speed** 143 kt (264 km/h); **Cruising speed** 120 kt (222 km/h); **Service ceiling** 16,400 ft (5,000 m); **Hover in Ground Effect** 9,350 ft (2,850 m); **Rate of climb** 1,770 ft/min (9 m/sec); **Length** 31.27 ft (9.53 m); **Height** 8.94 ft (2.72 m); **Rotor diameter** 34.46 ft (10.5 m); **Power plant** 1×Turbomeca Astazou IIIN2 (643 hp); **All-up weight** 4,189 lb (1,900 kg); **Empty weight** 1,874 lb (850 kg); **Payload** 2,026 lb (918 kg); **Weapons** None standard, but has provision for pod-mountings (see text).

The British Army's Gazelles resulted from the 1967 Anglo-French Helicopter Agreement, which also produced the Lynx and Puma. By this arrangement, the Aerospatiale design was partially manufactured and completely assembled by Westland Helicopters at Yeovil and Weston-Super-Mare. The initial production contract was for 29 helicopters, delivered between April 1973 and September 1974, and eventually some 212 were delivered. The first unit to be equipped was 660 Squadron (then with BAOR at Soest) and the last airframe was

delivered in 1984.

The Gazelle is a front-line observation helicopter, now equipped with the Ferranti AF 532 observation aid (known as GOA to the Army Air Corps) which operates with the Lynx/TOW in HELARM teams, designed to blunt the advance of enemy armour, especially in the Central Region of Germany. In addition, Gazelle helicopters attached to British Army of the Rhine are used for forward reconnaissance, border patrol, personnel transportation, casualty evacuation and specialist reconnaissance tasks. For the latter role, the Canadair CL-227 drone has been modified to make a reconnaissance pod.

In 1980, a flight of Gazelles was sent to Zimbabwe-Rhodesia to support the Monitoring Force and the air crew received considerable

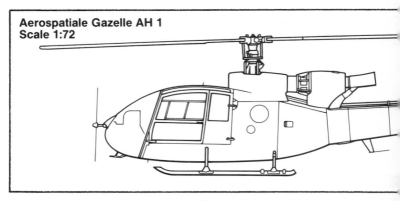

Aerospatiale Gazelle AH 1
Scale 1:72

praise from the Rhodesian Air Force helicopter crews for their flying skills and courage during this potentially dangerous period.

During the Falklands conflict, the Gazelles of 3rd Commando Brigade Air Squadron were armed with SNEB 68 mm rocket pods (similar to the ground-attack Harrier) to give some measure of self-protection but, in the event, the weapons were not used. In addition, cabin-mounted 7.62 mm General Purpose Machine Guns were carried. The SNEB is not however considered a standard weapon. Nevertheless, the helicopter proved its worth during Operation 'Corporate', although two were lost to Argentine ground fire and one, sadly, to a blue-on-blue engagement when it is believed that a Sea Dart missile from the guided missile destroyer HMS *Cardiff* brought

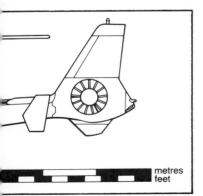

Above left *A Gazelle AH 1 during acceptance trials at Westland's factory.*

Above *A Gazelle carrying a reconnaissance pod in Germany. (*R P von Lutz*)*

Left *A Gazelle in Norway, supporting the Ace Mobile Force. (*British Army / UKLF*)*

Below *A Gazelle with the Nightsun lamp for surveillance duties in Northern Ireland.*

down a Gazelle with a Royal Signals party aboard who had been checking radio rebroadcast stations near San Carlos.

The Gazelle is currently operational, supporting British Forces in Belize where it replaced the Sioux, being considerably better for operations over the jungle terrain. At the other extreme of temperature, the Gazelle operates regularly in arctic Norway with the Ace Mobile Force, part of the British Army's commitment to NATO's northern flank area. In Northern Ireland, the Gazelle is used for a

variety of tasks, including aerial cover for street patrols, carrying the Spectrolab Nightsun searchlight and acting as a fast communications aircraft for military and government personnel.

Both Gazelle AH 1 and Lynx AH 1 airframes from Army Air Corps stocks are assigned to the 3rd Commando Brigade Air Squadron of the Royal Marines, the majority of whose air crew undergo flying training with the Army Air Corps at Middle Wallop.

According to the *Army Air Corps Journal*, 'the Gazelle is chic, lissom and athletic ... unmistakably foreign'.

Lynx AH 1

Westland Army Lynx: Purpose Anti-tank, liaison and command; **Crew** 1 pilot/aircrewman, 1 pilot/aircraft commander; **Passengers** Up to 9; **Maiden flight** 12 April 1972 (prototype), 11 February 1977 (production); **Service entry** 1977; **Range** 340 nm (630 km); **Max speed** 140 kt (259 km/h); **Cruising speed** 125 kt (232 km/h); **Service ceiling** 12,000 ft (3,660 m); **Hover in Ground Effect** Not Available; **Rate of climb** 2,170 ft/min (11 m/sec) **Length** 43.63 ft (13.3 m); **Height** 11.5 ft (3.5 m); **Rotor diameter** 42 ft (12.8 m); **Power plants** 2×Rolls -Royce Gem 2 turboshafts (900 shp each); **All-up weight** 9,600 (4,355 kg); **Empty weight** 6,773 lb (3,072 kg); **Payload** 3,894 lb (1,766 kg); **Weapons** 8×TOW anti-tank missiles; podded machine gun option (see text).

The initial concept of the Westland WG 13 Lynx was as a utility helicopter to carry squad-sized infantry, armed with anti-tank, mortar and other direct fire weapons. In this role, the helicopter was due to replace the Scout. With the adoption of the Scout/SS 11 missile combination, the role envisaged for the Lynx changed to that of primarily anti-tank helicopter, working in concert with the Gazelle (see above) as a highly effective and flexible blocking strike force.

The utility role is still carried out however in Northern Ireland, where the Lynx AH 1s of the resident units operate in an unarmed re-supply, trooping and light support role for the British Army and Royal Ulster. Its tasks include the positioning and collection of foot patrols in rural areas, resupplying the forward observation posts on the border with the Republic of Ireland, taking quick-reaction troops to the scene of an incident and allowing VCPs (vehicle check points) to be thrown up around a suspected terrorist position.

Only Scout and Gazelle light helicopters were sent to the Falkland Islands during the conflict but temporarily, during 1982–84, the Lynx was deployed to the Falklands Islands in the quick reaction role. It was later replaced by the Scout for budgetary and operational reasons.

In British Army of the Rhine, the Lynx AH 1 is deployed in three

Above *Westland's Lynx can be configured for trooping ...*

Left *... or for anti-tank operations, armed with the TOW missile. (*Rolls-Royce / British Army*)*

Above right *The Lynx / TOW is the backbone of BAOR AAC Regiments. (*Rolls-Royce*)*

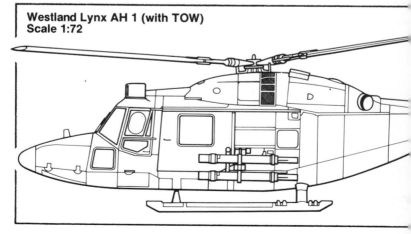

Westland Lynx AH 1 (with TOW)
Scale 1:72

regiments supporting corresponding armoured divisions, but there is also a command and control role for the helicopter at corps level. In 1986, experiments were undertaken to provide the helicopter with a better camouflage design for its operations in both the flat open North German Plain and the scattered hills and valleys further south and west, within the British Corps area.

The Lynx has been demonstrated with a large inventory of carried weapons, including SNEB and SNORA rockets, the Rockwell Hellfire laser-guided anti-armour missile, Oerlikon and Giat cannon and 7.62 mm podded machine gun installations. As far as is known, the British

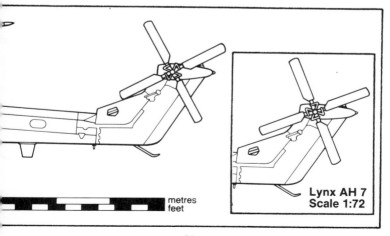

metres
feet

Lynx AH 7
Scale 1:72

Lynx can also be used to support airmobile operations, carrying Milan ground-based anti-tank teams. (Westland)

Army's requirement continues to be that the Lynx carries TOW (in its various modified forms) until the introduction of the light attack helicopter (see page 113) but after that time, the helicopter may be given a new role which will require it to be armed with different weapons.

Lynx AH 7

Westland Improved Army Lynx: Purpose Anti-tank, liaison and command **Crew** 1 pilot, 1 pilot/aircraft commander; **Passengers** Up to 9; **Maiden flight** 1986; **Service entry** 1987; **Range** 263 nm; **Max speed** 114 kt; **Cruising speed** 96 kt (177 km/h); **Service ceiling** 13,400 ft (4,085 m); **Hover in Ground Effect** 1,500 ft (3,720 m); **Rate of climb** 1,440 ft/min (7.2m/sec); **Length** 43.63 ft (13.3 m); **Height** 11.5 ft (3.5 m); **Rotor diameter** 42 ft (12.8m); **Power plant** 2×Rolls-Royce Gem 43-2-2 turboshafts (1,120 shp, 890 shp max continuous power); **All-up weight** 10,750 lb (4,876 kg); **Empty weight** 6,733 lb (3,072 kg); **Pay load** 3,894 lb (1,766 kg); **Weapons** 8×TOW anti-tank missiles; see Lynx AH 1 for alternatives.

Developed by Westland from an Army Air Corps requirement to redress some of some of the problems which have occurred with the

*First flown in November 1985, the Lynx AH 7 is the improved version of the Lynx/TOW combination and has been ordered for the Light Battlefield Support role. By April 1987 six of the type had been brought into front line service. (*Westland*)*

Lynx, including loss of tail rotor effectiveness, poor power in certain flight regimes and a general need to improve the helicopter's performance.

Besides the uprated Gem engines, the Lynx AH 7 has a new gearbox and the Westland 30 tail rotor, turning in the opposite direction to that of the original Mark 1, to provide better control in yaw. It is possible that the new helicopters will be fitted with a mission management system in due course.

In April 1987, the British government ordered a batch of 16 light support variants of the Lynx AH 7 to form a squadron, to support the newly created 24 Airmobile Brigade, to be based at Topcliffe in Yorkshire.

Lynx AH 5

Only one of this interim design was completed and it now operates on the Lynx development programme with the Ministry of Defence Procurement Executive at the Royal Aircraft Establishment, Bedford.

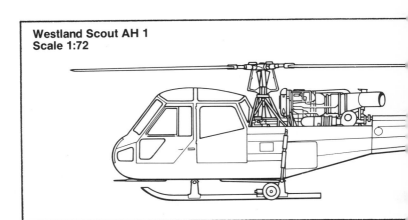

Westland Scout AH 1
Scale 1:72

Scout AH 1

Westland Scout: Purpose Light utility (later anti-tank); **Crew** 1 pilot, 1 aircrewman; **Passengers Up to** 5; **Maiden flight** 4 August 1960; **Service entry** 1963; **Range** 263 nm (488 km); **Max speed** 114 kt (211 km/h); **Cruising speed** 96 kt (177 km/h); **Service ceiling** 13,400 ft (4,085 m); **Hover in Ground Effect** 12,500 ft (3,720 m). **Rate of climb** 1,440 ft/min (7.2 m/sec); **Length** 30.33 ft (9.24 m); **Height** 8.92 ft (2.73 ft); **Rotor diameter** 32.25 ft (9.83 m); **Power plant** 1×Rolls-Royce/Bristol Nimbus 105 turboshaft (701 shp); **All-up weight** 5,350 lb (2,427 kg); **Empty weight** 3,232 lb (1,466 kg); **Payload** 2,048 lb (929 kg); **Weapons** 4×Nord SS 11 anti-tank missiles (obsolete); podded guns (see text).

Designed to be the first turbine-powered helicopter in the Army Air Corps, the Scout did not reach service until 1963 because of engine

Scout AH 1 operations along the frontier between Hong Kong and the People's Republic of China.

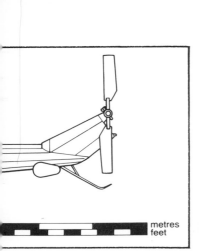

Early Scout operations were flown in Borneo and other 'hot spots'. (Robin Adshead)

problems. In fact, the Scout had a bad reputation early in its life, although today, it is 'loved' by its pilots, young or old.

Immediately on being brought into service, the first Scouts were in action in Borneo (during Confrontation with Indonesia) and later in the Radfan area of Aden as Britain withdrew from the Yemen peninsula. It was during these operations that the fixed 7.62 mm machine gun packs were developed for the helicopter and later a cabin-mounted gun was installed at the expense of the port-side fixed skid-mounting.

In 1964 it was decided to mount the French-designed Nord AS 11/

In 1964, the Scout was fitted with the Nord SS 11 wire-guided anti-tank missiles which were used in anger during the Falklands conflict. (British Army/HG 1 Div)

In 1986, the first British Army helicopter unit manned by the Territorial Army was formed flying the Scout. (Patrick Allen)

Above left *Special forces and other operations can be conducted from the very stable platform provided by the Scout. (JSPRS)*

SS.11 wire-guided anti-tank missiles to the Scout to provide British Army of the Rhine with a credible and flexible anti-tank ability. To aim the missiles, which were used operationally in the Falklands against Argentine 'sangers', the Ferranti AF 120 optical sight was mounted on the port-side cabin roof to be operated by the aircrewman/air gunner.

It is thought that the Scout provided the transport for the Special Air Service when the regiment dramatically broke the Iranian Embassy seige in London and certainly the helicopter has been shown as the fictional mount of the SAS. The helicopter has also been used in Northern Ireland to carry television cameras.

Overseas the helicopter remains in service with 660 Squadron AAC at Sek Kong, Hong Kong as the light helicopter support to the

British Forces and the Gurkha Field Force. During the illegal immigrant problems of the early 1980s, the helicopters were operating regular on 'Eagle Patrols' to rescue the IIs coming across the coastal flats, open estuaries and marshes from the People's Republic of China, seeking a new home in capitalist Hong Kong. For these operations, special rope scrambling nets were devised to allow a number of unfortunates to be rescued and brought to safe ground. Because of the regular overwater operations carried out by the Squadron, its Scouts are fitted with flotation gear above the cabin roof. Hong Kong-based Scouts are also deployed to Borneo in support of the Gurkha battalion stationed in the kingdom.

The Falkland Islands Squadron of the Army Air Corps operated the Scout for liaison, communications and utility work in support of the British garrison. Routine jobs included taking specialist troops to inspect communications installations and patrols to outlying islands.

In the United Kingdom, the Scout has a new role with 666 Squadron

666 Squadron AAC (V) in formation over one of Wiltshire's white horses.

AAC, as a United Kingdom Land Forces communications unit, mainly staffed by members of the Territorial Army. It is envisaged that the Scout will continue to support UKLF and Home Defence forces for some years.

For a casualty evacuation role, the Scout can be fitted with stretcher panniers on each side of the fuselage, making use of the skid undercarriage. In this role during the Falklands campaign some several dozen badly injured troops, especially from the Parachute Regiment and the Scots Guards were 'casevaced' to San Carlos for treatment and all who arrived at the field hospital lived. Captain Sam Drennan and Captain Richard Nunn, Royal Marines, were each awarded the Distinguished Flying Cross for extracting the wounded whilst under fire, the latter award was sadly posthumous after Lieutenant Nunn lost his life in the only Scout to be destroyed in the conflict, in an unequal contest with an Argentine Pucara ground-attack aircraft. In addition to the external stretcher cases, described by Lieutenant Colonel John Everett-Heath, author of *British Military Helicopters* (Arms & Armour Press, 1986), as having a resemblance to a coffin for a conscious occupant, casualties can be carried internally in a little more comfort but less practically because the Scout must be fitted with bulged cabin doors.

The Scout was the British Army's first turbine-helicopter and is seen here in an early military exercise.

FIXED-WING AIRCRAFT

After the Second World War, the existing air observation post and glider regiment units were nearly all disbanded. The glider squadron continued operations until late 1950 when it was phased out of British Army service, although the Glider Pilot Regiment was not disbanded until 1 September 1957 — the day that the Army Air Corps was formed.

From 1947 onwards, the British Army received the Auster AOP 6 and 7, which saw service world-wide, particularly in Korea, Malaya and Europe. These aircraft were replaced in the mid-1950s by the last of long line of Austers, the AOP 9. This was a rugged, three-seat air observation, communications and liaison aircraft. During the 1970s, the Auster AOP 9, although retired from operational duties in March 1967, was used for forward air controller and pilot training and the last aircraft was transferred to the AAC's Historic Aircraft Flight in September 1981.

For liaison tasks and general communications work, the British Army acquired a number of de Havilland Canada Beaver aircraft, and in 1986 this aircraft remains the last operational fixed-wing type (see below). Also from Canada, the de Havilland Canada Chipmunk has

Preserved by the Museum of Army Flying is this Taylorcraft Auster I, the first of a long line of Auster aircraft.

been in service since 1957 when the Army Air Corps commenced its own pilot training programme. A few Chipmunks remain in service at Middle Wallop (see below).

Beaver AL 1
de Havilland Canada DHC-2 Beaver: Purpose Liaison and special duties; **Crew** 1 pilot, 1 aircrewman; **Passengers** Up to 4; **Maiden flight** 16 August

Still in AAC service is the Canadian designed Beaver.

Beaver roles include supply drops using underwing racks.

1947; **Service entry** 1962; **Range** 637 nm (1,180 km); **Max speed** 140 kt (259 km/h); **Cruising speed** 124 kt (230 km/h); **Service ceiling** 18,000 ft (5,485 m); **Length** 30.25 ft (9.22 m); **Height** 9 ft (2.74 m); **Span** 48 ft (14.63 m); **Wing area** 250 sq ft (23.2 sq m); **Power plant** 1×Pratt & Whitney Wasp Junior R-985 radial engine (450 hp); **All-up weight** 5,100 lb (2,313 kg); **Empty weight** 2,850 lb (1,293 kg); **Payload** 1,000 lb (454 kg); **Weapons** None.

Some 46 of these Canadian-designed aircraft were delivered to the Army Air Corps from 1962 for short take-off and landing operations in support of the British Army in such places as Borneo, Aden and later Northern Ireland. The latter is the only operational location for the

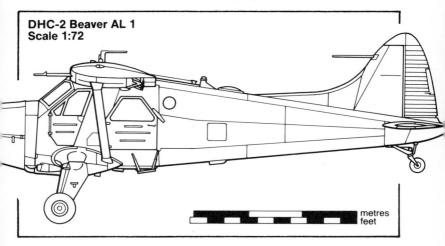

DHC-2 Beaver AL 1
Scale 1:72

metres
feet

A Beaver of 653 Squadron AAC carrying out deck landing practice in the aircraft carrier Centaur *in 1961. (Major John Dicksee)*

aircraft now, with a Flight being based at Aldergrove, near Belfast, from where it operates around the Province supporting various units, including being used for photographic reconnaissance.

It is understood that the Army Air Corps is seeking a replacement type for Northern Ireland duties, and the short-list includes the Pilatus Britten-Norman Defender.

Chipmunk T 10
de Havilland Canada DHC–1 Chipmunk: Purpose Basic training; **Crew** 1 pilot, 1 student; **Passengers** None; **Maiden flight** 22 May 1946; **Service**

Formation flypast of Chipmunk T 10 training aircraft.

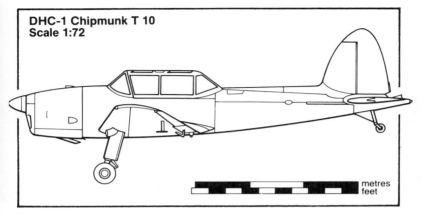

DHC-1 Chipmunk T 10
Scale 1:72

metres
feet

entry February 1953; **Range** 245 nm (454 km); **Max speed** 120 kt (220 km/h); **Cruising speed** 101 kt (187 km/h); **Service ceiling** 15,800 ft (4,815 m); **Length** 25.42 ft (7.75 m); **Height** 7 ft (2.13 m); **Span** 34.33 ft (10.5 m); **Wing area** 172 sq ft (15.97 sq m); **Power plant** 1×de Havilland Gipsy Major 8 piston engine (145 hp); **All-up weight** 2,014 lb (914 kg); **Empty weight** 1,425 lb (646 kg); **Weapons** None.

Over 700 Chipmunk trainers were delivered from the British production line to the British forces and the first for the Army arrived at Middle Wallop in February 1953, where it replaced the Tiger Moth bi-plane as the basic flying trainer. The Chipmunk remains in service with the Army Air Corps at Middle Wallop in the fixed-wing basic training role and with slight improvements is likely to continue in the role until the mid-1990s.

Still providing basic training, the Chipmunk will be replaced in the 1990s. (David Oliver)

HISTORIC AIRCRAFT
The Auster

This important aircraft in the history of British army flying and the Army Air Corps in particular was first manufactured by the British subsidiary of the American Taylorcraft company as early as 1938. The first Austers were built for civil customers before the Second World War but later the Royal Air Force took careful note of the high-wing aircraft's ability, especially to support the army's artillery spotting.

After approximately one hundred Auster Is were built, modifications were made to the aircraft's design, including the provision of trailing edge flaps to improve short take-off and landing capability, leading to the Auster II (with US-built engines) and the Auster III (with a de Havilland power plant).

Better accommodation for the pilot and a passenger was provided by the Auster IV, but of the wartime models the Auster V was the most numerous with some 800, almost half the total number of Austers built before and during the Second World War. British Austers were flown in almost every theatre of war after the invasion of North Africa, serving British, Commonwealth and Dutch units in the 2nd Tactical Air Force and the Desert Air Force.

*Auster IV provided good pilot and passenger accommodation. (*Museum of Army Flying*)*

Auster AOP 6 aircraft served worldwide after the Second World War. (Museum of Army Flying)

Auster AOP 6

Auster Aircraft Mk 6: Purpose Light liaison and observation; **Crew** 1 pilot, 1 observer/passenger; **Maiden flight** 1945; **Service entry** 1945 **Range** 275 nm (510 km); **Max speed** 108 knots (200 km/h); **Cruising speed** 94 knots (174 km/h); **Service ceiling** 14,000 ft (4,265 m); **Length** 23.75 ft (7.24 m); **Height** 8,375 ft (2.55 m); **Span** 36 ft (10.9 m); **Wing area** 184 sq ft (17.1 sq m); **Power plant** 1×de Havilland Gipsy Major 7 piston engine (145 hp) **All-up weight** 2,160 lb (980 kg); **Empty weight** 1,413 lb (641 kg); **Weapons** None; **Special equipment** Vertical camera and flares.

The American engined Auster IVs and Vs were replaced by the British-powered Auster AOP 6 in 1945; initial production continued until 1949 but its use in Malaya, Korea and other trouble spots ensured that the lines were opened again in 1952. By 1955, the various faults of the AOP 6 were rectified in the AOP 9, a totally new design.

Auster AOP 9

Auster Aircraft Mk 9: Purpose Light liaison and observation; **Crew** 1 pilot, 1/2 observers/passengers; **Maiden flight** 19 March 1954; **Service entry** February 1955; **Range** 210 nm (389 km); **Max speed** 110 knots (204 km/h); **Cruising speed** 96 knots (177 km/h); **Service ceiling** 19,500 ft (5,945 m); **Length** 23.708 ft (7.23 m); **Height** 8.92 ft (2.72 m); **Span** 36.42 (11.1 m); **Wing area** 197.5 sq ft (18.35 sq m); **Power plant** 1×Blackburn Cirrus Bombardier 203 piston engine (180 hp); **All-up weight** 2,330 lb (1,057 kg); **Empty weight** 1,590 lb (721 kg); **Weapons** None; **Special equipment** Camera and flares.

The Korean War had shown just how useful the helicopter would become in the modern battlefield, so the service life of the Auster AOP 9 in the British Army was bound to be short-lived. Nevertheless, the AOP 9 was a valuable and useful aircraft fort air observation post, casualty evacuation, photographic reconnaissance, liaison, utility and even cable laying tasks. The Auster AOP 9 first entered service with 656 Squadron, then still a Royal Air Force unit, and was engaged in operations against terrorist groups in Malaya before going into action in Aden. It was a totally new design as compared to the AOP 6, including the adoption of large, low-pressure tyres for the rugged landing gear.

The Skeeter

Between the wars, the Cierva Autogiro Company built autogiros, some of which were tested and impressed into service 'for the Duration' by the British Air Ministry. After the Second World War had ended, the company began work on several helicopter projects, including a light helicopter, named the Skeeter. Originally, the design was for a training and general purpose helicopter for the civilian market and then the Royal Navy took a major interest in it.

It was not until development had led to the Mk 6 version that there seems to have been real interest in the project from the Air Ministry who were looking for a helicopter to fulfil the aerial observation post needs of the British Army. By then the Cierva company had been taken over by Saunders Roe but since it was planned that the new helicopter would enter service in 1957, the Skeeter was ruled out in favour of the Fairey Ultra Light Helicopter because of the production forecasts for both types. In 1956, due to the lack of finance available to Fairey, the Skeeter became the favourite for the AOP contract.

Despite its simplicity and lack of battlefield effectiveness, the Skeeter showed that the helicopter had potential.

Skeeter AOP 12

Saunders Roe Skeeter 7A: Purpose Light observation and utility helicopter; **Crew** 1 pilot, 1 observer/passenger; **Maiden flight** 1956; **Service entry** August 1958; **Range** 185 nm (343 km); **Max speed** 90 knots (167 km/h); **Cruising speed** 75 knots (139 km/h); **Service ceiling** 12,800 ft (3,900 m); **Length** (fuselage) 26.5 ft (8.1 m); **Height** 7.5 ft (2.29 m); **Rotor diameter** 32 ft (9.76 m); **Power plant** 1×de Havilland Gipsy Major piston engine (215 hp); **All-up weight** 2,300 lb (1,043 kg); **Empty weight** 1,653 lb (750 kg); **Weapons** None.

Although service trials were carried out with the Skeeter AOP 6, it was the AOP 10 which entered service evaluation and the AOP 12 which became the standard service helicopter. Records show that 64 were built for the Army Air Corps with orders placed between 1956 and 1959, deliveries being between August 1958 and July 1960. By the time that the last Skeeter had been delivered, Saunders Roe had also been taken over by Westland, now Britain's only helicopter manufacture.

Army Air Corps instructors were trained at the Royal Air Force Central Flying School on dual-control Skeeter AOP 12s and in turn these QHI (Qualified Helicopter Instructors) trained army pilots, officers and NCOs at Middle Wallop.

The Skeeter suffered from a chronic lack of power and was only truly operational in the United Kingdom and supporting the British Army of the Rhine; the Army Air Corps had to wait until the arrival of

The Skeeter suffered from a chronic lack of power.

the Westland Scout before it had a helicopter which could be operated in hot/high overseas locations. The helicopter made a major contribution to army flying and is remembered with great affection at Middle Wallop and other AAC locations.

Sioux AH 1

Westland (Agusta-Bell) 47G-3B1: Purpose Light observation and liaison helicopter; **Crew** 1 pilot, 1/2 observers/passengers; **Maiden flight** 9 March 1965; **Service entry** 1965; **Range** 190 nm (351 km); **Max speed** 91 knots (169 km/h); **Cruising speed** 75 knots (138 km/h); **Service ceiling** 20,000 ft (6,100 m); **Length** 32.33 ft (9.85 m); **Height** 9,313 ft (2.84 m); **Rotor diameter** 37.125 ft (11.32 m); **Power plant** 1×Avco Lycoming TVO-435-B1A piston engine (270 hp); **All-up weight** 2,950 lb (1,338 kg); **Empty weight** 1,794 lb (814 kg).

The American designed Bell 47 first flew in December 1945, but 20

The Westland-Agusta built Sioux AH 1 serving with the Gurkha Air Troop in Borneo in May 1967. (Robin Adshead)

The first officially-formed Army Air Corps display team was the Blue Eagles, flying the Sioux AH 1 in a series of five helicopter formations. The team was extremely successful and did much to publicize the flying role of the British Army. (AACC)

years later became the first aircraft to offically bear the title 'Royal Marines' and was the eagerly-awaited replacement for the Skeeter helicopter. It was especially welcomed in the Far East, where armed versions were used to give suppressive fire to ground troops via the medium of the 7.62 mm general-purpose machine gun.

In Northern Ireland, where the Sioux served for almost ten years, it was already in the country, based at Belfast, Omagh and Londonderry, when the present Troubles began. The helicopter achieved fame in its support role for the British army and the Royal Ulster Constabulary, carrying the Spectrolab Nightsun searchlight which had been developed for the American forces in Vietnam. Military spouses and civilian workers were often carried by helicopter in the more remote areas.

Apart from Northern Ireland and Borneo, the helicopter served the Army Air Corps well in Belize (during the border dispute with neighbouring Guatemala), Cyprus and Aden. At home, four helicopters from Middle Wallop made up the Blue Eagles display team and the helicopter was used for training. It is well loved by those who trained on it, despite its twist grip throttle and piston engine, and the need to be a contortionist to change radio frequencies.

WEAPONS AND ROLE EQUIPMENT

Air-launched weapons

Although various trials were carried out with armed helicopters at the Joint Experimental Helicopter Unit (JETU) at Middle Wallop during the 1950s, including the mounting of machine-guns for self-defence purposes, it was not until the advent of the reliable guided missile that the prospect of an effective armed helicopter was born. Used in conjunction with a gyroscopically stabilized sight and a guidance system, the missile can be deadly against tanks as has been demonstrated in the closing days of the American involvement in Vietnam, during the Israeli invasion of Lebanon in 1982 and in the protracted Iraq–Iran 'Gulf' conflict.

In 1967, the British Army held firing trials which demonstrated the accuracy of a wire-guided missile fired from a helicopter and from 1970, the Scout was declared operational. It was armed with the Sud Aviation (now Aerospatiale) SS.11 missile system, directly through a Avimo-Ferranti AF 120 optical sight. This system was taken to the Falkland Islands in 1982 and successfully used against reinforced Argentine positions on the outskirts of Port Stanley. In addition, the

*An SS 11 wire-guided missile leaves a Scout during firing trials on Salisbury Plain. (*AAC Centre)

Falkland Islands saw the fitting of the 68 mm SNEB aerial rocket pods on a number of Gazelle AH 1 helicopters but for several reasons, including the exposure of the helicopter in barren terrain, the system has not been adopted for general use.

The primary weapon of the Army Air Corps today is the Hughes Aircraft Corporation TOW anti-tank missile, carried by the Lynx AH 1 and soon by the Lynx AH 7 (see below). Future developments may well include an advanced, fire-and-forget anti-tank missile, laser-guidance systems and self-defence missiles. These are also discussed below.

TOW

Hughes Aircraft Corporation: Range 500 to 3,750 m; **Missile length** 1.168 m; **Missile body diameter** 0.152 m; **Weight at launcher** Approx 24 kg; **Max velocity** <Mach 1; **Armour penetration** >400 mm; **Sight magnification** 2× or 13× optics; **Missile manoeuvre range** + 110 azimuth, + 30 elevation

Airborne TOW (Tube-launched, Optically tracked, Wire-guided)

missile system is a semi-automatic anti-tank weapon system with a stand-off range outside all but the most modern low level anti-aircraft systems on the battlefield. The Army Air Corps' Lynx carry up to eight missiles, four on each side of the helicopter.

TOW roof sight The missiles are loaded in their launcher units which are normally slaved in elevation with the sightline of the TOW roof-mounted stabilized sight. The sight is manufactured in the United

Above left *Purchased from France at the beginning of the Falklands campaign, the SNEB 68 mm rocket launcher was not used but proved an important morale booster. (British Army)*

Above *Developed by Hughes Aircraft of California, the TOW is an effective anti-tank missile. (Westland)*

Right *For firing TOW, the Lynx is fitted with the British Aerospace/Hughes Aircraft roof-mounted sight on the port side of the helicopter. (British Army/HQ 1 Armoured Div)*

Kingdom by British Aerospace's Army Weapons Division at Stevenage, north of London, in co-operation with Hughes Aircraft Corporation of California. Operated by the co-pilot/gunner, the sight consists of a dual magnification, direct pointing stabilized telescope with a periscopic relief. Included in the sight is an integral triple magnification infra-red tracker, the axes of which are accurately boresighted with the optical axis defined by the sight's eyepiece reticle. It is a modified version of the M65 sight found on the Bell Cobra and McDonnell Douglas Defender.

Night sight In 1986 it was announced that British Aerospace, together with Rank Pullin Controls, had been awarded a British Army contract to update the system to allow for inclusion of a thermal imaging module (Forward Looking Infra-Red) which senses the natural radiation from the target to give true night and adverse weather vision/firing capability, bringing the Lynx/TOW combination into line with infantry, artillery and tank systems on the battlefield. Targets are visible through many types of smoke screen, mist and thin cloud, as well as camouflage. The system will be operational in 1988.

In 1986, it was announced that the TOW roof sight would be given the Pullin Controls thermal imaging module for better adverse weather and a night firing capability. (BAe)

Future updates could include the provision of a Laser Range Finding facility.

Gunner's task To launch a TOW missile at an enemy tank, the gunner's primary task is to acquire and track the target with the sight, maintaining the reticle crosswires on the centre of the target during the missile's flight time. This is achieved by means of a pressure control stick which points the optical system in azimuth and elevation. The launcher tubes are inclined upwards with respect to the line-of-sight and prior to the missile launch, the pilot (in the righthand seat) is required to align the Lynx with the target bearing within a small magnitude of error. The gunner then operates the 'fire' button, the launch sequence is initiated and the missile launch motor ignites, burning for some 50 milliseconds to expel the missile from the tube. The flight motor boosts the missile for nearly 2 seconds to a velocity of just below Mach 1, allowing it to coast onto the target.

Flight control of the TOW missile is achieved by the use of winglets which unfold when it leaves the tube. After launch, a Xenon arc beacon is ignited on the after end of the missile to act as an infra-red (IR) source for detection by the tracker. This source is filtered so that it does not disturb the operator's view of the target. When the missile is within the IR field, sensors detect the beacon and hence measure missile displacement from the gunner's line-of-sight to the target. Angular error signals are developed in the guidance electronics and steering commands going to the missile via the wire link.

Improved TOW During the middle and late 1980s, it is envisaged that the TOW missile has undergone and will undergo further improvement programmes to ensure that it is capable of meeting the threats of the 1990s. From 1997 onwards, it is presumed that the tri-

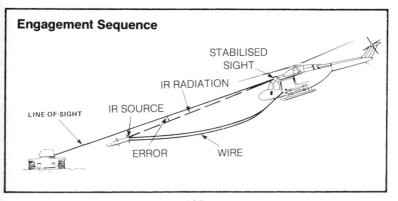

Engagement Sequence

STABILISED SIGHT

IR RADIATION

IR SOURCE

LINE-OF-SIGHT

ERROR

WIRE

national third generation missile programme (see page 117) — or Trigat — will have developed an effective helicopter-launched weapon for use by the Light Attack Helicopter and other battlefield helicopter developments.

Amongst the developments planned for TOW is the provision of a new fuzing system, designed and manufactured by Thorn EMI Electronics, which will allow 'top attack' techniques to be used against enemy main battle tanks. This is where the missile uses a laser profile to establish its exact location over a tank and then detonates its warhead with the blast directed downwards to the most vulnerable part of the tank, the top of the turret.

A major concern for air crew remains the in-flight elapsed time from missile launch until its strikes its target, this being especially relevant in hostile environments where the helicopter's survivability will be diminished by the exposure to counter attack whilst the missile is in flight.

Special equipment

In common with other battlefield helicopter forces, the Army Air Corps has developed and acquired a number of specialist equipment systems for regular and not-so-regular use. Role-fits are dictated by operation requirements and, like the foot soldiers which army helicopters support in Northern Ireland, there is some specialist equipment developed for that demanding internal security role.

Night vision goggles From the early 1980s, trials have been carried out with night vision goggles (NVG), including the use in Northern Ireland of the full-face Passive NVG and the US Army's ANVIS system of image intensifiers which have been used in various locations. In 1986, it was announced that Ferranti had won an order from the UK Ministry of Defence to supply the Nite-Op lightweight NVG and this equipment will be adopted by the Army Air Corps. The major problem facing the use of NVG in helicopters is the need to make the cockpit lighting NVG-compatible so that instrument lights do not affect the pilot's view through the helicopter windscreen.

CAP Scientific MIC This is a small hand-held calculator developed to assist Gazelle and Lynx crews with simple mission management problems, such as the decoding of radio messages. It is the forerunner to an aircraft-mounted mission management system.

Canadair recce pod In British Army of the Rhine, trials have been carried out with the AN/USD-501 Midge reconnaissance drone's pod, mounted to the port side of a Gazelle helicopter. The Midge carries Zeiss stereoscopic tri-lens optics for panchromatic or infra-

Right *Dressed to fight at night and in nuclear-biological-chemical conditions, the modern AAC aircrew is shown with ANVIS night vision goggles. (*AAC Centre)

Below *For better reconnaissance capability, almost all Gazelle AH 1s will be fitted with the Ferranti AF 532 observation aid. (*Ferranti)

red imagery. This is a task carried out by any Squadron nominated to support artillery and is described as a role fit undertaken at first line.

Ferranti AF 532 GOA The Gazelle Observation Aid was first operationally tested during Exercise 'Lionheart' in September 1984 and since then the Army Air Corps' Gazelle force has been steadily updated with the equipment. The GOA is mounted on the port side cabin roof of the helicopter, using Avimo/Ferranti equipment to provide the aircrewman or aircraft commander with an observation tool, capable of ×2.5 or ×10 magnification. The aid is used to search for and identify possible targets for the Lynx/TOW or for reconnais-

sance purposes. In the future it will be updated to take a laser target marker and a laser range finder to enhance its capability for directing Lynx/TOW HELARM operations.

GEC Avionics Heli-Tele This commercial television outside broadcast system has been used effectively in such places as Northern Ireland to assist with day and night observation of potential trouble spots and to film IRA and Loyalist demonstrations.

Racal cockpit management systems Known as RAMS (Racal Avionics Management System), the cockpit management system has been under trials from the manufacturer for several years in a Lynx AH 1 from the Trials and Development Flight at Middle Wallop. It may form the basis for a system in the future light attack helicopter programme.

Racal TANS This Doppler-based navigation system is fitted to all Army Air Corps Lynx helicopters and gives an accuracy of about four per cent over a day's flying. It is used as an aid to the air crew, who still fly with maps and do not depend on the system. It has however proved extremely reliable and is invaluable to nap-of-the-Earth and HELARM operations.

Racal Mini-TANS More correctly the Racal Decca Doppler 80 lightweight navigation aid which has the same basic purpose as the TANS (above) but without so many navigational waypoints. It is fitted to the Gazelle AH 1.

Exhaust suppression kits All helicopters can be fitted with exhaust suppression kits which deflect the hot exhaust gases away from the helicopter to be broken up by the main rotor disc in flight. This

Right *The peacetime Scout pilot with DPM two-piece flying suit, Mk IV flying helmet, aircrew lifejacket, flying boots and gloves. (*British Army/UKLF)

Below left *CAP Scientific's mission information computer system is the first step towards the full scale development of a mission management system in British Army helicopters. (*CAP)

is a basic survivability measure against the use of heat-seeking missiles by an enemy or by terrorists. The Gazelle is most commonly seen with the equipment.

Specialist flying gear

The Army Air Corps is very much an integrated part of the British Army but, like many branches of the Service, its soldiers require specialist clothing for specific tasks.

Flying clothing The modern Army Air Corps air crew no longer wear flying suits for operational tasks overseas and flying operations in British Army of the Rhine, the official service dress is now the two-piece temperature DPM combat dress.

NBC suit and respirator For wartime operations in a full-threat environment it is inevitable that air crew will wear nuclear-biological-chemical suits, called 'noddy suits'. The main suit is a two-piece

garment in olive drab, charcoal impregnated paper. Black disposable gloves and flying boot coveralls are also worn. It is thought that this gear will be replaced by a new Disruptive Pattern Material suit. The Avon AR 5 pilot's respirator is worn under the flying helmet.

Flying helmet All Army Air Corps flying helmets are manufactured by Helmets Limited and the present model is the lightweight Mark IVc which incorporates Racal Acoustics microphone/earphone units. Some helmets have been modified to take night vision goggles.

Army Air Corps specialist uniform

Light blue beret Since 1957, permanent cadre members of the Army Air Corps wear the 'sky blue' beret with the silver eagle cap badge within a crowned wreath on a square dark blue patch. Senior NCOs wear a light blue eagle edged dark blue above their chevrons.

Air gunner A special skills badge is on a dark blue ground with a yellow G within a crowned ring with a single light blue wing to the left side, worn on the left breast.

Left *Medium alert state NBC (nuclear biological chemical) conditions which can quickly be brought up to full alert status with the addition of the aircrew (AR 5) or ground troop S 6 / S 10 respirator, and if applicable, steel helmet. (*Rolls-Royce)

Right and below *The most modern operational headwear for the AAC aircrew is the Helmets Ltd Mk IV system with Racal Acoustics microphone. Sergeant Gary Smith AAC is modelling the helmet in the right-hand seat of the Lynx and is wearing the one-piece Nomex flying suit and old pattern (but comfortable) flying gloves. (*AACC)

(Clockwise) Pilot, Air Gunner and Air Observer wings in dark cotton for battledress wear in tactical situations. (AACC)

Air observer As above but the G is replaced by an O.

Pilot A crowned lion standing on a crown between light blue wings, worn on the left breast.

FUTURE PROGRAMMES

FUTURE AIRCRAFT PROJECTS

As the perceived threat to the modern battlefield continues to grow so the Army Air Corps, as one of the British Army's main direct fire elements, finds ways of countering that threat. Since the early 1980s, paper studies and other evalutions have been undertaken into a variety of equipment, including a completely new helicopter design and associated new weapons. In addition, there has been consider-able debate about the need for a fixed-wing aircraft to act as Corps Area radar picket and electronic missions aircraft. These studies are continuing but their importance to the future of the Army Air Corps means that they must be explained here.

Light attack helicopter

In September 1986 the British government and industry joined with its counterparts in Italy, Spain and the Netherlands to sign a memoran-dum of understanding which would allow for the development of a new generation of dedicated light attack helicopter. The British interest in such a project goes back to July 1984 when a General Staff target was issued for a tandem seat, two-place attack helicopter to be armed with the third generation or Trigat missile (see below).

This new concept is known as the light attack helicopter (LAH) and unlike the previous two types of battlefield anti-tank helicopter, it is intended that it should be designed from stratch as an anti-tank weapon system. To that end there is bound to be a requirement for it to be capable of stand-off anti-tank action, self-defence, armed reconnaissance and forward air controller for both artillery and fighter ground attack aircraft. Amongst the physical requirements should be agility, manoeuvrability and reliability, with ease of operation and maintainability also involved in the design.

In the four-nation design study, known as the Tonal programme, is successful, then the first helicopters could be in service by 1997. It would be based on the twin-engined Agusta A129 light attack helicopter which enters Italian Army service at the end of 1987 but which itself is not suitable for the more demanding Central Region role which the Army Air Corps has at present.

ASTOR/Britten-Norman Defender

In 1984, the UK Ministry of Defence announced a competition to select a special stand-off radar surveillance system for use over the

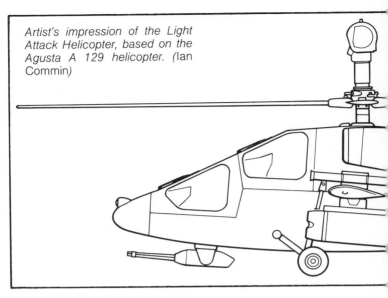

Artist's impression of the Light Attack Helicopter, based on the Agusta A 129 helicopter. (Ian Commin)

Westland Helicopters worked hard to convince the Army Air Corps that needed the Lynx-3 multi-role battlefield helicopter, pictured here arme with the Rockwell Hellfire laser-guided missile and 20 mm cannon By 1987, it seems that the Tonal multi-national programme will b selected instead. (Westland)

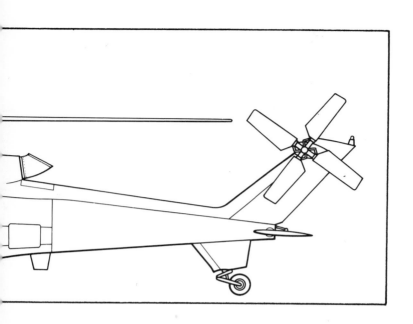

A possible candidate for the area stand-off radar system is the Pilatus Britten-Norman Defender with radar manufactured by Thorn-EMI Electronics or Ferranti Defence Systems. (PBN)

future battlefield. Two companies, Ferranti Radar Systems and Thorn EMI Electronics are competing for the radar, called ASTOR (Area STand Off Radar) which has been fitted to the nose of a Britten-Norman Defender aircraft as a generic aircraft for the Technical Demonstrator Programme.

The radar system is designed to give the British Corps headquarters in Germany advanced warning of enemy troops and other movements behind the front line by measures of secure data link transfer of information. The aircraft selected will also be used as a command post for the direction of the GEC Avionics Phoenix remotely piloted vehicle.

At the time of going to print, no decision had been made on the procurement of the system for the British Army, but if and when the decision is made, it will fall to the Army Air Corps to operate it in British Army of the Rhine.

Light battlefield helicopter

An order, placed in April 1987, is the first step towards re-equipping the support helicopter formations for the British Army. The 16 unarmed Lynx AH 7 helicopters will be manned by the Army Air Corps and will be delivered in 1988/89. The helicopters will be tasked with supplementing the RAF Puma squadrons and providing lift for 24 Bde as a forerunner to a new regiment in the North of England to support 2 Division at York.

In addition, planners at the Directorate at Middle Wallop have been investigating a new light battlefield helicopter design with the

In April 1987 it was announced that 25 utility versions of the EH 101 would be procured for the Puma light support helicopter replacement programme. It is possible that this helicopter will be flown and operated by the British Army rather than by an RAF proxy. (Westland)

reliability, survivability and maintainability attributes of the Light Attack Helicopter for the late 1990s and the next century. It is possible that common components will be used for both types.

With the order for EH 101 utility helicopters to replace the RAF Puma force in the 1990s, it is possible that the Army Air Corps will be able to take over the light and intermediate lift support to the British Army, leaving the RAF with the Chinook force only. This would bring the United Kingdom more into line with her NATO partners. Unlike most other nations, the UK operates a split between light (AAC) and intermediate/medium (RAF) support helicopters which means that the Wessex, Puma and Chinook fleets are not under army control, unlike the AAC Gazelle and Lynx assets.

The Army Air Corps has already commenced the two-pilot training programme (see page 123) and it is thought that it could be in a position to man the Lynx LSHs in late 1988, about the time that the new Airmobile Brigade will be nominated for the role in support of BAOR. The new brigade will be able to move its men and equipment to block enemy advances and act as a special reserve for the divisional commanders, defending the 1 (BR) Corps area.

FUTURE WEAPONS

Forward planners in NATO have perceived the need for new weapons to counter the advances in main battle tank and other armoured vehicle design being made by the Warsaw Pact. Amongst the anti-tank missile attributes of the future will be the ability to select and lock-on to a target after launch, allowing the launcher (helicopter) to manoeuvre away from the engagement zone before counter-attack is possible. To protect the anti-tank helicopter, considered an important target for roving Soviet helicopters, a new anti-helicopter missile is being developed which will also be effective against fixed-wing aircraft.

As self-defence for light support helicopters in the forward battle-field, considerable effort has been made to develop a gun turret which can be used by the pilot to suppress enemy ground fire. The Army Air Corps is understood to be studying this sytem.

These weapons may not come into service in the future, but they are described here to give an indication of the advances being made in the technology for the battlefield helicopter and it is unlikely that the Army Air Corps will be without such systems in the next decade.

Trigat

This is the multi-national programme to develop a long-range anti-

The Mi-24 (NATO: Hind) could have an operational role of attacking British Army anti-tank helicopters in the event of a future conflict. (W W Duck)

armour missile, with a secondary anti-air role, capable of destroying the latest and planned enemy tanks and other armoured vehicles. It will be designed as a fire-and-forget weapon, possibly laser guided with an independent homing head. British Aerospace is heading the British side of the programme in collaboration with MBB and Aerospatiale.

Starstreak

In December 1986, it was announced that the British Army would buy the ground-based Shorts Starstreak to enter service in about 1990. This beam-riding weapon has applications for helicopter self-defence and might be developed if funding is made available.

Javelin

In the early 1980s, work was carried out to attempt to make the Javelin shoulder-launched anti-aircraft missile capable with the Gazelle but the tests were unsuccessful. It is believed in some quarters that proper research funding of the project would have resulted in a successful conclusion.

Lucas turret

Demonstrated to the British Army in 1986, the 12.7 mm Lucas gun turret is designed to fit most Western types of light support and combat

118

It is possible that the future light battlefield helicopter will be armed with the Lucas 12.7 mm gun turret for self-defence and close support; the turret can also be used for TOW and air-to-air missiles.

helicopters, linked to a Ferranti helmet-mounted sight, to provide suppressive fire against ground forces, especially for resupply and trooping tasks. Future developments of the gun turret could include the use of fire-and-forget anti-helicopter missiles, like Starstreak or other weapons.

SPECIAL EQUIPMENT

Although weapons and airframes form an important part of any new equipment buy for military forces, there are also certain specialist pieces of kit which are necessary to make that equipment work. In the case of the Army Air Corps, this means special mission equipment which will enhance the helicopter's role as an observation and direct fire vehicle. Two examples of special equipment likely to be introduced to Army Air Corps service are described below.

Mast-mounted sights

Developed by both American and European concerns, the mast-mounted sight gives the helicopter carrying the system the advantage of being able to remain below the horizon and yet observe (and even attack) an enemy on the far side without giving away its position by 'unmasking'. The MMS is mounted above the rotor disc and the images it sees are transferred electronically to the observer in the helicopter.

Racal's Prophet radar warning system which is thought to have been offered to the Army Air Corps; the cockpit display for the Gazelle is mounted on the left side of the instrument panel.

The MMS system is ideal for reconnaissance and the marking of enemy armour vehicles for attack by separately positioned attack helicopters working in concert with a team leader carrying an MMS. For the future light attack helicopter programme, it is possible that a British manufactured mast-mounted sight will be ordered to give the helicopter the ability to undertake its own reconnaissance, observation and fire control from a stand-off and survivable position.

Radar warning receivers

Urgently required for the Gazelle and Lynx helicopters operating in support of the British Army of the Rhine, a good radar warning receiver system would alert the crew to attack from radar-directed missiles or guns, from ground or aerial attackers. In other battlefield aviation forces, including the medium support helicopters of the RAF, there have been RWR systems available for some years.

In 1987, a UK Ministry of Defence sponsored competition between the leading British defence avionics companies (some with American partners) will have come to fruition and a system will be chosen to retrofit to existing helicopters and to be updated, prior to integration in the light attack helicopter.

TRAINING AND TACTICS

TRAINING

Any professional and specialist group requires a sound training doctrine to allow it to function correctly and of course the armed forces have particular needs. The Army Air Corps is justifiably proud of its training standards which have developed over the last thirty years to a level which is envied by other battlefield helicopter forces around the world. The professional standards achieved were well proven during the Falklands conflict in 1982.

Since the introduction of armed helicopters and the ability of the Army Air Corps to operate as a direct fire combat arm, with the predominant role of armed action in the NATO Central Region, the training of air-crew has evolved to compliment the needs of full integration with infantry, artillery and the armoured units of the battlefield. The Army Air Corps draws a significant proportion of its pilots and aircrewmen from most Corps, Arms and Services of the modern British Army.

Air crew

In 1973 the role of the aircrewman was introduced to supplement the pilot who was obviously unable, except in certain non-combat

Co-operation in Germany: a Royal Marines Gazelle light observation helicopter at an AAC squadron location. Note the use of an old parachute to cover the helicopter's canopy to prevent sun glint.

situations, to fly and fight the helicopter simultaneously. The aircrewman was given the task of operating the observation and weapon systems, but also had to be capable of flying the helicopter to safe landing, should the pilot become incapacitated.

The Army Air Corps has been faced with the problem of integrating the armed and highly potent helicopter into the modern battlefield, including the demands which the new systems, such as the night capable TOW, bring with them. Air crew cockpit workload is already high in a helicopter and in combat it must increase to such levels that the aircraft's survivability — and therefore that of the air crew and any passengers — could overload the combined abilities of a pilot and aircrewman.

The pilot not only has to fly the helicopter but until recently was also the tactical commander of the aircraft, section, Flight or squadron. Commander and driver functions can no longer be combined in one man, especially as he is unable to use the observation aid/weapon sight and fly the aircraft nap-of-the-Earth. In combat, the pilot would be totally dependent on the aircrewman for vital information which would allow the helicopter to discharge its primary function — armed section.

In the Army Air Corps, the aircrewman could frequently be a junior non-commissioned office who would be without the necessary tactical training nor command experience. In battle it could be dangerous and wasteful of expertise and resources.

Improved system of crewing

From 1 January 1987 the Army Air Corps has adopted a two-pilot helicopter air crew training programme, known universally as CREST (aircraft Crew RESTructuring). The aircraft commander will now be an experienced pilot (senior non-commissioned officer or commissioned officer) who will occupy the left-hand seat (with the observation aid/sight) from where he will be responsible for all aspects of the helicopter's effective operation. The responsibility of flying the aircraft will rest with the pilot in the right-hand seat but the aircraft commander will be able to assist him as necessary.

The tactical commander as well as the aircraft commander, the more experienced pilot will be able to fight the helicopter effectively, using the various weapon and sensor systems to the best advantage, as well as making better tactical assessments and judgements. Not least is the belief that the new system will allow for better flight safety because (as with the Federal German and French army aviation corps) the pilot will be able to concentrate on flying the helicopter.

Obviously part of the driving force behind the CREST system is the introduction of the light attack helicopter, the Army Air Corps's first wholly dedicated fighting helicopter which is due to be introduced in the late 1990s.

Officer entry After successfully completing the Army Pilot Course, an officer pilot spends a period of time as a helicopter pilot (in the right hand seat) gaining experience before moving to the Aircraft Com-

Left *High standards of flying are required of army aviators, including the ability to fly under wires during nap-of-the-Earth flight moving up to a fire team rendezvous point.*

Right *Events such as the British Helicopter Championships encourage continued professionalism and a close co-ordination between pilot and aircrewman.*

mander Course and later the Flight Commander Course.

NCO entry Under the CREST system, the minimum rank of NCO pilots will be reduced to Corporal (from Sergeant) but Lance Corporals of four years service will be eligible for pilot training, being promoted to the rank of acting Corporal on joining the Army Pilot Course. Corporal pilots will be able to progress to become aircraft commanders with the rank of Sergeant.

Army Pilot Course
After selection at Biggin Hill, a special selection board at Middle Wallop and a flying grading course, the potential helicopter pilot will be required to undertake a 150-hour Army Pilot Course which includes fixed-wing and helicopter training as well as basic instrument flying. Some tactical training may be undertaken but the bulk will be gained under the supervision of an aircraft commander once the pilot joins a squadron or Flight. The course will lead to the presentation of Army Wings.

Lynx conversion
Under the CREST programme, new Lynx air crew will progress from

In the late 1970s, a considerable number of pilots and aircrewmen were converted from the Scout (right) to the new Lynx helicopter. From 1986, under the CREST programme, many aircrewmen are becoming pilots to allow the senior member of the flight crew to control the missile system. (Rolls-Royce)

basic flying training to a conversion to Lynx at Middle Wallop. Other pilots will remain on Gazelle training but there seems to be a need to qualify as many pilots and aircraft commanders as possible for the Lynx. A typical Lynx conversion will take thirty hours and for the Gazelle (direct from basic flying training) some 36 hours.

TACTICS
Anti-tank helicopter doctrine

The major role of the helicopter in supporting NATO forces in Germany is that of anti-tank operations, which the Army refers to as HELARM tasks. This is basically a mobile and highly flexible operation to counter the possibility of Warsaw Pact armoured advances across the Inner German Border which separates West and East Germany. Commander Aviation, British Army of the Rhine is tasked to provide three regiments of battlefield helicopters whose main function is to carry out HELARM tasks.

Each regiment has three squadrons of a combined force of reconnaissance Gazelle AH 1 helicopters which support the Westland Lynx AH 1 anti-tank helicopters armed with the Hughes Aircraft

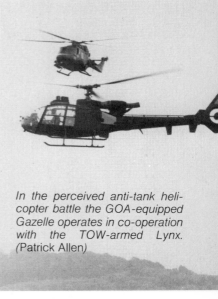

In the perceived anti-tank helicopter battle the GOA-equipped Gazelle operates in co-operation with the TOW-armed Lynx. (Patrick Allen)

| 1 | | 2 | | 3 | | 4 |

Gazelle HELARM Commander moves into position to monitor enemy advance

HELARM called to forward rendezvous point (in cover of farm), helicopters on ground to conserve fuel

HELARM fire team moves into firing position where Lynx pop-up' to engage enemy with TOW

Warsaw pact tanks and vehicles engaged and destroyed

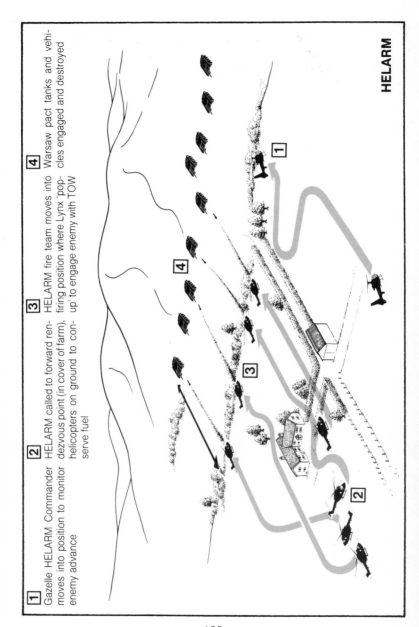

HELARM

Corporation's Improved TOW missile system. Guided by the Gazelles, Lynx helicopters would provide anti-tank missile HELARM to block an enemy advance or breakthrough, using the inherent flexibility of the helicopter to move rapidly from sector to sector if needs be.

In the modern, fast-moving scenario of warfare in the NATO Central Region, the general principles involved vary little. Across the variety of terrain, engagement scenarios and weather conditions which might occur in the BAOR area of the predominantly flat North German Plain is an area where massed counter attacks against tank formations would tend to be foreseen and, to the south and west, the hills and woods would probably be ideal for small attack team ambushes.

Initial reconnaissance and intelligence about enemy movements would come from ground-based or helicopter sources, filtered through to army helicopter units from Divisional Headquarters. The Gazelle would work in pairs, leap frogging up to the engagement area. Although NATO operates a defensive battlefield doctrine and the best anti-tank helicopter ambush positions have already been viewed and decided upon, it will still be necessary for helicopter observation, using the Ferranti GOA and other observation aids, to establish

With the enemy armour in the 'killing zone', the Lynx commander launches the missile whilst the pilot keeps the helicopter within launch constraints. (British Aerospace)

enemy tank concentrations and anti-aircraft defences. A plan to engage the enemy can then be made, with best possible use of the ground features to achieve surprise.

When the enemy's position is known, the Lynx move into firing positions with a Gazelle acting as overseer, in contact with the formation headquarters having received the approval for HELARM. The Lynx reach the firing positions flying as tactically as possible, using nap-of-the-earth techniques, to a pre-planned final rendezvous point where the helicopters will take up defensive positions on the ground until the commander is ready to call them forward to the actual firing position.

This close to the forward edge of the battle area, the time at the loitering position should be limited because of possible surprise by enemy helicopter or ground forces and it will depend on what is actually happening to the enemy. Ideally, prior to HELARM, artillery should be brought to bear to close-down the tanks and make the job of spotting the attacking helicopters more difficult. As the enemy column enters the planned engagement zone the Lynx are called forward to fire one or two TOW missiles when the tanks are at the optimum stand-off range for the missile system.

The reconnaissance Gazelles will often be required to locate new fire positions for the Lynx after the first salvos in order to reduce the exposure time of the missle-launching helicopters to return fire from the enemy tanks and self-propelled anti-aircraft artillery. Not only does the two-man crew of the Lynx have its work cut-out engaging an enemy tank every 30 seconds or so but the reconnaissance and command Gazelle air crews will be working 'like one-armed paper hangers', flying tactically to avoid detection and yet giving the HELARM commander the necessary intelligence for him to carry out his function of killing tanks.

Through the medium of computerized war games, following Israeli lessons learned in conflict with Syria in Lebanon and frequent exercises in Germany HELARM has been proved to work on paper; it has been shown that a Lynx HELARM formation can destroy many more than twice its own number of tanks in a matter of minutes. The priority is always to kill command tanks first but it may be necessary to remove air defence vehicles from the battlefield first, depending on the tactical situation.

Forward reconnaissance

Another of the more important tasks of the modern battlefield helicopter force is reconnaissance and it is a role of the light

Above *After a HELARM attack, the Lynx fire team moves back to the Forward Arming and Refuelling Point, here set up in a field next to a wood.*

Below *Re-arming and refuelling should take a matter of minutes before the helicopters can launch and take up another attack position. Note the light grey/green painted Lynx on the right.*

129

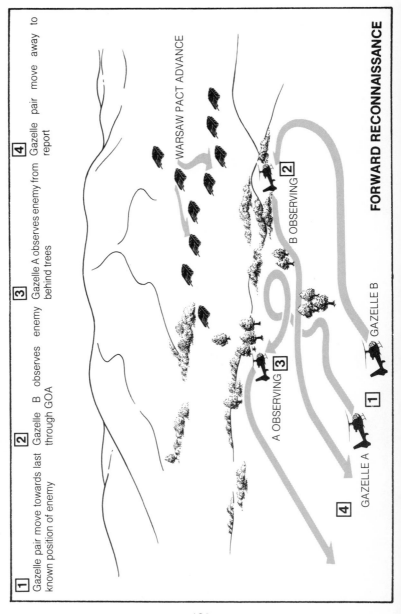

1 Gazelle pair move towards last known position of enemy

2 Gazelle B observes enemy through GOA

3 Gazelle A observes enemy behind trees

4 Gazelle A observes enemy from Gazelle pair move away to report

WARSAW PACT ADVANCE

B OBSERVING **2**

GAZELLE B

1

A OBSERVING **3**

GAZELLE A

4

FORWARD RECONNAISSANCE

observation helicopter to undertake this task in the Army Air Corps. Future survivability demands may mean however that an armed reconnaissance helicopter will be required and a study group is presently looking at this task in relation to the future light attack helicopter (see page 113).

Amongst the needs of the battlefield commander is one of knowing exactly what the enemy is doing all the time; this obviously is not always possible, but helicopters help to increase its likelihood in war. The Army Air Corps, supporting 1 (BR) Corps in the NATO Central Region provides a unit — 664 Squadron — which works closely with ground-based 'screen' reconnaissance units, including those equipped with the Scimitar and Scorpion light tank (or Combat Vehicle Reconnaissance (Tracked) in British Army parlance). In addition, each of the three regiments based in Federal Germany supports its assigned Division with Gazelles (and occasionally Lynx) for reconnaissance.

To aid this role, the Gazelle has been progressively equipped with the Ferranti Gazelle Observation Aid (GOA) during the last few years. This device is used for both observation/reconnaissance sorties and for supporting HELARM anti-tank helicopter operations.

Looking for the enemy, a Gazelle uses a wood as background cover during an exercise. (Patrick Allen)

For forward reconnaissance on the battlefield, two Gazelles normally operate together in an operation known as 'recce in pairs' where they use a leap-frogging technique to keep each other and the enemy in sight and yet remain undetected for as long as possible. In such operations, the light helicopters are potentially vulnerable to small arms fire from advance enemy reconnaissance parties, marauding enemy helicopters and fighter aircraft. Thus forward reconnaissance requires well trained, experienced and disciplined air crew.

Moving into contact with the enemy is a difficult and slow flying operation, requiring the use of what is termed 'nap-of-the-earth' technique. At no time should the Gazelles fly through the same airspace and they should operate without the use of radio contact wherever possible. The Gazelle has yet to be fitted with any self-defence systems, either passive types like radar warning receivers or active systems such as a guided air-to-air weapon.

Passive radar warning devices will help a Gazelle crew survive in a hostile environment. (Racal)

Right and below *How to land in the snow without loosing perspective. The incoming helicopter is guided on to a level landing sight by a colleague who has identified the wind direction and strength. As the helicopter approaches the landing site, the ground-based crewman provides a contrasting mass for the incoming pilot to focus on and give perspective. The landing will be a limited run-on so that snow does not recirculate back into the engine intake and cause a flame-out.* (British Army/UKLF)

From 1987, Lynx/TOW helicopters will acquire a night firing capability to support ground troops during the 24-Hour Battle. (BAe)

One of the most important areas of search and reconnaissance is the flank where the enemy could advance, surprise and overwhelm an unprepared commander. Helicopters with their flexibility and rapidity of movement are able to move into and out of the flank area, or can be called in to investigate contacts made by ground troops. It is thought the Warsaw Pact powers actually use helicopters for reconnaissance by contact where they determine enemy strengths by being engaged and even suffering losses. The Army Air Corps is not disposed to throwing away its valuable helicopters in this way nor to risking its even more valuable air crew in such operations.

Reconnaissance and observation of the battlefield still represents a vital function of the battlefield helicopter and recent exercises have shown its need. Hopefully, it will not be proved in war.

INDEX